LAPLACE TRANSFORM TABLES AND THEOREMS

LAPLACE TRANSFORM TABLES AND THEOREMS

Paul A. McCollum
Oklahoma State University

Buck F. Brown
Louisiana Polytechnic Institute

Holt, Rinehart and Winston
New York Chicago San Francisco Toronto London

Library of Congress Catalog Card Number: 65-18173
25548-0115
Printed in the United States of America

Portions of this book were published in
Laplace Transform Tables and Related Topics on Operational Methods, copyright © 1964 by
the Office of Engineering Research, Oklahoma
State University.

PREFACE

The dynamics of linear physical systems has been subjected to a great deal of investigation. For the most part, the emphasis has been on operational methods, and in particular on the Laplace transformation. In spite of this wide acceptance of transform methods, the authors have long been convinced that a need existed for a comprehensive yet concise listing of transform pairs, along with their associated properties. Armed with this belief and encouraged by the popularity of a table assembled by Dr. D. L. Johnson in 1951, the authors undertook a project to fulfill this need. The ultimate objective was to arrive at a listing whose form and order would prove fast and easy to use, yet maintaining accuracy at an unquestionably high level.

Chapter 1 contains the resultant tables of transform pairs; it is the culmination of an effort extending over several years. Chapter 2 contains a brief statement of many transform properties, along with an example of each; Chapter 3 presents and reviews some of the often encountered properties and theorems related to complex functions and the dynamics of physical systems. The ordering has been purposely chosen to minimize the effort required for repeated use of the tables. Each chapter has been written as an entity, and presents its material in a self-contained and independent manner, allowing for ease of reference to specific items, yet providing a source for more detailed study through the interrelationships among these items.

Throughout the tables and text the mathematical notation is that commonly encountered in linear system theory. For example, the generally accepted designation of the step function, $U_{-1}(\tau)$, where

$$U_{-1}(\tau) = \begin{cases} 0 \text{ for } \tau < 0 \\ 1 \text{ for } \tau \geq 0 \end{cases}$$

has been used extensively without the accompanying definition. Every effort has been made to clarify less usual notation by including a statement and/or a defining relationship.

The tables are organized first with regard to transform numerators, and then subgrouped according to denominators. A few minutes spent scanning the details of arrangement will undoubtedly enhance table utility. The constants involved in the transforms may, in general, assume any value, real or complex, except that multiple or higher order poles may not be created where none existed previously.

It should be mentioned that no table, however comprehensive, can replace a thorough understanding of transform techniques. As a matter of fact, a sound knowledge of the fundamentals is essential to intelligent use of the tables, so that the material contained herein is intended to supplement and not substitute for this understanding.

The authors wish to express appreciation to Dr. Clark A. Dunn and Dr. Joseph J. Norton, of the Office of Engineering Research at the Oklahoma State University, for their support and encouragement. Special mention is due Mr. Eldon Hardy for his perseverance and fine drafting. Thanks also are extended to Miss Velda Davis for her careful typing of the final text.

Stillwater, Oklahoma
Ruston, Louisiana
January 1965

Paul A. McCollum
Buck F. Brown

CONTENTS

Chapter 1

TABLES OF LAPLACE TRANSFORM PAIRS

TABLE I

LAPLACE TRANSFORM GENERAL PROPERTIES

NO.	NAME	F(s)	f(t)
1	Direct Laplace Transform	$\int_0^\infty f(t)\epsilon^{-st}dt$	$f(t)$
2	Inverse Laplace Transformation	$F(s)$	$\frac{1}{2\pi j}\int_{c-j\infty}^{c+j\infty} F(s)\epsilon^{st}dt$
3	Linearity	$F_1(s) \pm F_2(s)$	$f_1(t) \pm f_2(t)$
4	Linearity	$aF(s)$ where a is independent of s and t	$af(t)$
5	Real Differentiation	$SF(s)-f(0+)$	$\frac{df(t)}{dt}$
6	Real Differentiation	$S^nF(s)-\sum_{\ell=1}^{n} s^{(\ell-1)}\cdot f^{(n-\ell)}(0+)$ where $f^{(n-\ell)}(0+) \equiv \left.\frac{d^{(n-\ell)}f}{dt^{(n-\ell)}}\right\|_{t=0+}$	$\frac{d^nf(t)}{dt^n}$
7	Real Indefinite Integration	$\frac{1}{s}F(s)+\frac{1}{s}\int^{0+} f(t)dt$	$\int f(t)dt$
8	Real Definite Integration	$\frac{1}{s}F(s)$	$\int_0^t f(t)dt$
9	Real Definite Integration	$\frac{1}{s^2}F(s)$	$\int_0^t\int_0^\gamma f(\lambda)d\lambda d\gamma$
10	Real Definite Integration	$\frac{1}{s}\int_0^s F(r)dr$	$\int_0^\infty \frac{f(\gamma)}{\gamma}d\gamma$
11	Real Translation	$\epsilon^{-as}F(s)$ a is a non-negative real number	$f(t-a)\cdot U(t-a)$ where $U(t-a)$ is a unit step at $t=a$.
12	Real Translation	$\epsilon^{as}F(s)$ a is a non-negative real number	$f(t+a)$ if $f(t+a)=0$ when $-a<t<0$
13	Multiplication by s	$SF(s)$	$\frac{df(t)}{dt}$ if $f(0+)=0$
14	Division by s	$\frac{1}{s}F(s)$	$\int_0^t f(t)dt$
15	Complex Multiplication	$F(s)\cdot G(s)$	$\int_0^t f(t-\tau)\cdot g(\tau)d\tau$
16	Complex Differentiation	$\frac{dF(s)}{ds}$	$-tf(t)$
17	Complex Differentiation	$\frac{d^nF(s)}{ds^n}$	$(-1)^n t^n f(t)$ $n=1,2,\cdots$

$L\frac{di}{dt} + Ri = Vu(t) \rightarrow L[sI(s) - i(0)] + R\,I(s) = \frac{V}{s}$

NO.	NAME	F(s)	f(t)
18	Complex Integration	$\int_s^{\infty} F(s)ds$	$\frac{1}{t} f(t)$
19	Complex Translation	$F(s+a)$ a complex with non-negative real part.	$\epsilon^{-at} f(t)$
20	Complex Translation	$F(s-a)$ a complex with non-negative real part.	$\epsilon^{at} f(t)$
21	Scale Change	$F(as)$ a positive and independent of s and t.	$\frac{1}{a} f(\frac{t}{a})$
22	Differentiation with respect to a second independent variable.	$\frac{\partial F(s,r)}{\partial r}$ r independent of s and t.	$\frac{\partial f(t,r)}{\partial r}$
23	Integration with respect to a second independent variable.	$\int_{r_0}^{r} F(s,r)dr$ where r is independent of s and t.	$\int_{r_0}^{r} f(t,r)dr$
24	Commutativity of Laplace transformation with real transformation.	$\mathrm{Re}\left[F(s)\right]$	$\mathrm{Re}\left[f(t)\right]$ f(t) is a complex function.
25	Commutativity of Laplace transformation with imaginary transformation.	$\mathrm{Im}\left[F(s)\right]$	$\mathrm{Im}\left[f(t)\right]$ f(t) is a complex function
26	Final Value	$\lim_{s \to 0} sF(s) = \lim_{t \to \infty} f(t)$ sF(s) analytic on the axis of imaginaries and in the right half plane.	
27	Initial Value	$\lim_{s \to \infty} sF(s) = \lim_{t \to 0} f(t)$	

$\frac{1}{c}\int i\,dt + i\,dt + Ri = V\,u\,t$ $\qquad \mathcal{L}[f'(t)] = sF(s) - f(0)$

$\frac{1}{c}\left[\frac{I(s)}{s} + \frac{q(0)}{s}\right] + R\,I(s) = \frac{V}{s}$ $\qquad \mathcal{L}\left[f^{-1}(t)\right] = \frac{1}{s}\left[F(s) + \frac{1}{s} f^{-1}(0)\right]$

TABLE 2

GENERAL TABLE OF LAPLACE TRANSFORM PAIRS

ITS INVERSE TRANSFORM IS

IS THE LAPLACE TRANSFORM OF

NO.	F(s)	f(t)
1	s^N	$\delta^n(t)$ An impulse of order (N+1) at t=o where N is a positive integer.
2	s	$\delta'(t)$ A doublet impulse at t=o.
3	1	$\delta(t)$ A unit impulse at t=o. $\delta(t)=\infty$ when t=o; $\delta(t)=o$ otherwise.
4	$\frac{1}{s}$	$1 = u_{-1}(t)$ A unit step at t=o. $u_{-1}(t)=1$ when $t \geq o$; $u_{-1}(t)=o$ when $t < o$
5	$\frac{1}{s^2}$	t
6	$\frac{1}{s^N}$	$\frac{t^{(N-1)}}{(N-1)!}$ Where N is a positive integer.
7	$\frac{1}{s^N}$	$\frac{t^{(N-1)}}{\Gamma(N)}$ $\Gamma(N)$ is the gamma function.
8	$\frac{1}{\sqrt{s}}$	$\frac{1}{\sqrt{\pi t}}$
9	$\frac{1}{s^{3/2}}$	$2\sqrt{\frac{t}{\pi}}$
10	$\frac{1}{s+a}$	ϵ^{-at} Valid for complex a.
11	$\frac{1}{s(s+a)}$	$\frac{1}{a}(1-\epsilon^{-at})$
12	$\frac{1}{s^2(s+a)}$	$\frac{1}{a^2}(\epsilon^{-at}+at-1)$
13	$\frac{1}{s^3(s+a)}$	$\frac{1}{a^2}\left[\frac{1}{a}-t+\frac{at^2}{2}-\frac{1}{a}\epsilon^{-at}\right]$
14	$\frac{1}{(s+a)(s+b)}$	$\frac{1}{(b-a)}(\epsilon^{-at}-\epsilon^{-bt})$
15	$\frac{1}{s(s+a)(s+b)}$	$\frac{1}{ab}\left[1+\frac{1}{(a-b)}(b\epsilon^{-at}-a\epsilon^{-bt})\right]$
16	$\frac{1}{s^2(s+a)(s+b)}$	$\frac{1}{(ab)^2}\left[\frac{1}{(a-b)}(a^2\epsilon^{-bt}-b^2\epsilon^{-at})+abt-a-b\right]$
17	$\frac{1}{s^3(s+a)(s+b)}$	$\frac{1}{(ab)}\left[\frac{a^3-b^3}{(ab)^2(a-b)}+\frac{1}{2}t^2-\frac{(a+b)}{ab}t+\frac{1}{(a-b)}\left(\frac{b}{a^2}\epsilon^{-at}-\frac{a}{b^2}\epsilon^{-bt}\right)\right]$

NO.	F(s)	f(t)
18	$\frac{1}{(s+a)(s+b)(s+c)}$	$\frac{1}{(b-a)(c-a)}\epsilon^{-at}+\frac{1}{(a-b)(c-b)}\epsilon^{-bt}+\frac{1}{(a-c)(b-c)}\epsilon^{-ct}$
19	$\frac{1}{s(s+a)(s+b)(s+c)}$	$\frac{1}{abc}-\frac{1}{a(b-a)(c-a)}\epsilon^{-at}-\frac{1}{b(a-b)(c-b)}\epsilon^{-bt}-\frac{1}{c(a-c)(b-c)}\epsilon^{-ct}$
20	$\frac{1}{s^2(s+a)(s+b)(s+c)}$	$\frac{ab(ct-1)-ac-bc}{(abc)^2}+\frac{1}{a^2(b-a)(c-a)}\epsilon^{-at}+\frac{1}{b^2(a-b)(c-b)}\epsilon^{-bt}+\frac{1}{c^2(a-c)(b-c)}\epsilon^{-ct}$
21	$\frac{1}{s^3(s+a)(s+b)(s+c)}$	$\frac{1}{(abc)^3}\left[(ab+ac+bc)^2-abc(a+b+c)\right]-\frac{ab+ac+bc}{(abc)^2}t+\frac{1}{2abc}t^2$ $-\frac{1}{a^3(b-a)(c-a)}\epsilon^{-at}-\frac{1}{b^3(a-b)(c-b)}\epsilon^{-bt}-\frac{1}{c^3(a-c)(b-c)}\epsilon^{-ct}$
22	$\frac{1}{(s+a)^2}$	$t\epsilon^{-at}$
23	$\frac{1}{(s+a)^N}$	$\frac{t^{(N-1)}\epsilon^{-at}}{(N-1)!}$ Where N is a positive integer.
24	$\frac{1}{s(s+a)^2}$	$\frac{1}{a^2}\left[1-\epsilon^{-at}-at\epsilon^{-at}\right]$
25	$\frac{1}{s^2(s+a)^2}$	$\frac{1}{a^3}\left[at-2+at\epsilon^{-at}+2\epsilon^{-at}\right]$
26	$\frac{1}{s(s+a)^3}$	$\frac{1}{a^3}\left[1-\left(\frac{1}{2}a^2t^2+at+1\right)\epsilon^{-at}\right]$
27	$\frac{1}{(s+a)(s+b)^2}$	$\frac{1}{(a-b)^2}\left\{\epsilon^{-at}+\left[(a-b)t-1\right]\epsilon^{-bt}\right\}$
28	$\frac{1}{s(s+a)(s+b)^2}$	$\frac{1}{ab^2}-\frac{1}{a(a-b)^2}\epsilon^{-at}-\left[\frac{1}{b(a-b)}t+\frac{a-2b}{b^2(a-b)^2}\right]\epsilon^{-bt}$
29	$\frac{1}{s^2(s+a)(s+b)^2}$	$\frac{1}{a^2(b-a)^2}\epsilon^{-at}+\frac{1}{ab^2}\left(t-\frac{1}{a}-\frac{2}{b}\right)+\left[\frac{1}{b^2(a-b)}t+\frac{2(a-b)-b}{b^3(b-a)^2}\right]\epsilon^{-bt}$
30	$\frac{1}{(s+a)(s+b)(s+c)^2}$	$\left[\frac{1}{(c-b)(c-a)}t+\frac{2c-a-b}{(c-a)^2(c-b)^2}\right]\epsilon^{-ct}+\frac{1}{(b-a)(c-a)^2}\epsilon^{-at}+\frac{1}{(a-b)(c-b)^2}\epsilon^{-bt}$
31	$\frac{1}{s(s+a)(s+b)(s+c)^2}$	$\frac{1}{abc^2}+\frac{1}{a(a-b)(c-a)^2}\epsilon^{-at}+\frac{1}{b(b-a)(c-b)^2}\epsilon^{-bt}$ $+\left[\frac{1}{c(c-b)(a-c)}t-\frac{(c-b)(c-a)+c(2c-b-a)}{c^2(c-b)^2(c-a)^2}\right]\epsilon^{-ct}$
32	$\frac{1}{s^2(s+a)(s+b)(s+c)^2}$	$\left[\frac{1}{c^2(c-b)(c-a)}t+\frac{2(c-b)(c-a)+c(2c-b-a)}{c^3(c-b)^2(c-a)^2}\right]\epsilon^{-ct}+\frac{1}{a^2(b-a)(c-a)^2}\epsilon^{-at}$ $+\frac{1}{abc^2}\left(t-\frac{2}{c}-\frac{1}{a}-\frac{1}{b}\right)+\frac{1}{b^2(a-b)(c-b)^2}\epsilon^{-bt}$
33	$\frac{1}{(s+a)^2(s+b)^2}$	$\frac{1}{(b-a)^2}t\epsilon^{-at}-\frac{2}{(b-a)^3}\epsilon^{-at}+\frac{1}{(a-b)^2}t\epsilon^{-bt}-\frac{2}{(a-b)^3}\epsilon^{-bt}$

NO.	F(s)	f(t)
34	$\frac{1}{s(s+a)^2(s+b)^2}$	$\frac{(3a-b)}{a^2(b-a)^3}\epsilon^{-at} - \frac{1}{a(b-a)^2}t\epsilon^{-at} + \frac{(3b-a)}{b^2(a-b)^3}\epsilon^{-bt} - \frac{1}{b(a-b)^2}t\epsilon^{-bt} + \frac{1}{a^2 b^2}$
35	$\frac{1}{s^2(s+a)^2(s+b)^2}$	$\frac{2(b-2a)}{a^3(b-a)^3}\epsilon^{-at} + \frac{1}{a^2(b-a)^2}t\epsilon^{-at} + \frac{2(a-2b)}{b^3(a-b)^3}\epsilon^{-bt} + \frac{1}{b^2(a-b)^2}t\epsilon^{-bt}$ $+ \frac{1}{a^2 b^2}t - \frac{2(a+b)}{a^3 b^3}$
36	$\frac{1}{(s+a)(s+b)^2(s+c)^2}$	$\frac{1}{(b-a)^2(c-a)^2}\epsilon^{-at} + \frac{[3c-(b+2a)]}{(b-c)^3(a-c)^2}\epsilon^{-ct} + \frac{1}{(a-c)(b-c)^2}t\epsilon^{-ct} + \frac{[3b-(c+2a)]}{(a-b)^2(c-b)^3}\epsilon^{-bt}$ $+ \frac{1}{(a-b)(c-b)^2}t\epsilon^{-bt}$
37	$\frac{1}{s^2+\omega^2}$	$\frac{1}{\omega}\sin\omega t$
38	$\frac{1}{s(s^2+\omega^2)}$	$\frac{1}{\omega^2}(1-\cos\omega t)$
39	$\frac{1}{s^2(s^2+\omega^2)}$	$\frac{1}{\omega^2}t - \frac{1}{\omega^3}\sin\omega t$
40	$\frac{1}{s^3(s^2+\omega^2)}$	$\frac{1}{\omega^4}(\cos\omega t-1) + \frac{1}{2\omega^2}t^2$
41	$\frac{1}{(s+a)(s^2+\omega^2)}$	$\frac{1}{a^2+\omega^2}\epsilon^{-at} + \frac{1}{\omega\sqrt{a^2+\omega^2}}\sin(\omega t-\phi)$; $\phi=\tan^{-1}\left(\frac{\omega}{a}\right)$
42	$\frac{1}{s(s+a)(s^2+\omega^2)}$	$\frac{1}{a\omega^2} - \frac{1}{a^2+\omega^2}\left(\frac{1}{\omega}\sin\omega t + \frac{a}{\omega^2}\cos\omega t + \frac{1}{a}\epsilon^{-at}\right)$
43	$\frac{1}{s^2(s+a)(s^2+\omega^2)}$	$\frac{1}{a\omega^2}t - \frac{1}{a^2\omega^2} + \frac{1}{a^2(a^2+\omega^2)}\epsilon^{-at} + \frac{1}{\omega^3\sqrt{a^2+\omega^2}}\cos(\omega t+\phi)$; $\phi=\tan^{-1}\left(\frac{a}{\omega}\right)$
44	$\frac{1}{(s+a)(s+b)(s^2+\omega^2)}$	$\frac{1}{(b-a)(a^2+\omega^2)}\epsilon^{-at} + \frac{1}{(a-b)(b^2+\omega^2)}\epsilon^{-bt} + \frac{1}{\omega\sqrt{\omega^2(a+b)^2+(ab-\omega^2)^2}}\sin(\omega t-\phi)$ $\phi=\tan^{-1}\left(\frac{\omega}{a}\right)+\tan^{-1}\left(\frac{\omega}{b}\right)$
45	$\frac{1}{s(s+a)(s+b)(s^2+\omega^2)}$	$\frac{1}{ab\omega^2} + \frac{1}{a(a-b)(a^2+\omega^2)}\epsilon^{-at} + \frac{1}{b(b-a)(b^2+\omega^2)}\epsilon^{-bt}$ $- \frac{1}{\omega^2\sqrt{\omega^2(a+b)^2+(ab-\omega^2)^2}}\cos(\omega t+\phi)$; $\phi=\tan^{-1}\left(\frac{b}{\omega}\right)+\tan^{-1}\left(\frac{a}{\omega}\right)$
46	$\frac{1}{s^2(s+a)(s+b)(s^2+\omega^2)}$	$\frac{1}{ab\omega^2}\left(t-\frac{1}{a}-\frac{1}{b}\right) + \frac{1}{a^2(b-a)(a^2+\omega^2)}\epsilon^{-at} + \frac{1}{b^2(a-b)(b^2+\omega^2)}\epsilon^{-bt}$ $- \frac{1}{\omega^3\sqrt{\omega^2(a+b)^2+(ab-\omega^2)^2}}\cos(\omega t+\phi)$; $\phi=\tan^{-1}\left(\frac{b}{\omega}\right)-\tan^{-1}\left(\frac{\omega}{a}\right)$
47	$\frac{1}{(s+a)^2(s^2+\omega^2)}$	$\frac{1}{\omega(a^2+\omega^2)}\sin(\omega t-\phi) + \left[\frac{1}{a^2+\omega^2}t + \frac{2a}{(a^2+\omega^2)^2}\right]\epsilon^{-at}$; $\phi=2\tan^{-1}\left(\frac{\omega}{a}\right)$

NO.	F(s)	f(t)
48	$\frac{1}{s(s+a)^2(s^2+\omega^2)}$	$\frac{1}{a^2\omega^2} - \frac{1}{\omega^2(a^2+\omega^2)}\sin(\omega t+\phi) - \left[\frac{1}{a(a^2+\omega^2)}t + \frac{3a^2+\omega^2}{a^2(a^2+\omega^2)^2}\right]\epsilon^{-at}$ $\phi = \tan^{-1}\left(\frac{a}{\omega}\right) - \tan^{-1}\left(\frac{\omega}{a}\right)$
49	$\frac{1}{s^2(s+a)^2(s^2+\omega^2)}$	$\frac{1}{\omega^3(a^2+\omega^2)}\sin(\omega t+\phi) + \frac{1}{a^2(a^2+\omega^2)}t\epsilon^{-at} + \frac{2(2a^2+\omega^2)}{a^3(a^2+\omega^2)^2}\epsilon^{-at} + \frac{1}{a^2\omega^2}t - \frac{2}{a^3\omega^2}$ $\phi = 2\tan^{-1}\left(\frac{a}{\omega}\right)$
50	$\frac{1}{(s+a)(s+b)^2(s^2+\omega^2)}$	$\frac{1}{\omega(b^2+\omega^2)\sqrt{a^2+\omega^2}}\sin(\omega t-\phi) + \frac{1}{(a-b)(b^2+\omega^2)}t\epsilon^{-bt} + \left[\frac{2(a-b)b-(\omega^2+b^2)}{(a-b)^2(b^2+\omega^2)^2}\right]\epsilon^{-bt}$ $+ \frac{1}{(a^2+\omega^2)(b-a)^2}\epsilon^{-at}$; $\phi = 2\tan^{-1}\left(\frac{\omega}{b}\right) + \tan^{-1}\left(\frac{\omega}{a}\right)$
51	$\frac{1}{(s+a)^2(s+b)^2(s^2+\omega^2)}$	$\frac{1}{\omega(a^2+\omega^2)(b^2+\omega^2)}\sin(\omega t+\phi) - 2\left[\frac{(a^2+\omega^2)-a(b-a)}{(a^2+\omega^2)^2(b-a)^3}\right]\epsilon^{-at} + \frac{1}{(a^2+\omega^2)(b-a)^2}t\epsilon^{-at}$ $-2\left[\frac{b^2+\omega^2-b(a-b)}{(b^2+\omega^2)^2(a-b)^3}\right]\epsilon^{-bt} + \frac{1}{(b^2+\omega^2)(a-b)^2}t\epsilon^{-bt}$ $\phi = 2\tan^{-1}\left(\frac{b}{\omega}\right) + 2\tan^{-1}\left(\frac{a}{\omega}\right)$
52	$\frac{1}{(s^2+a^2)^2}$	$\frac{1}{2a^3}\left[\sin at - at\cos at\right]$
53	$\frac{1}{s(s^2+a^2)^2}$	$\frac{1}{a^4}(1-\cos at) - \frac{1}{2a^3}t\sin at$
54	$\frac{1}{s^2(s^2+a^2)^2}$	$-\frac{3}{2a^5}\sin at + \frac{1}{a^4}t\left(1+\frac{1}{2}\cos at\right)$
55	$\frac{1}{(s+a)(s^2+\omega^2)^2}$	$\frac{1}{(a^2+\omega^2)^2}\epsilon^{-at} - \frac{1}{2\omega^2\sqrt{(a^2+\omega^2)}}t\sin(\omega t+\phi_1) - \frac{\sqrt{(a^2+4\omega^2)}}{2\omega^3(a^2+\omega^2)}\cos(\omega t+\phi_2)$ $\phi_1 = \tan^{-1}\left(\frac{a}{\omega}\right)$, $\phi_2 = \tan^{-1}\left[\frac{a(a^2+3\omega^2)}{2\omega^3}\right]$
56	$\frac{1}{s(s+a)(s^2+\omega^2)^2}$	$\frac{1}{\omega^4 a} - \frac{1}{a(a^2+\omega^2)^2}\epsilon^{-at} + \frac{1}{2\omega^3\sqrt{(a^2+\omega^2)}}t\cos(\omega t+\phi_1) - \frac{\sqrt{4a^2+9\omega^2}}{2\omega^4(a^2+\omega^2)}\cos(\omega t+\phi_2)$ $\phi_1 = \tan^{-1}\left(\frac{a}{\omega}\right)$, $\phi_2 = \tan^{-1}\left(\frac{3\omega}{2a}\right) - 2\tan^{-1}\left(\frac{\omega}{a}\right)$
57	$\frac{1}{s^2(s+a)(s^2+\omega^2)^2}$	$\frac{1}{\omega^4 a}t - \frac{1}{\omega^4 a^2} + \frac{1}{2\omega^4\sqrt{(a^2+\omega^2)}}t\sin(\omega t+\phi_1) - \frac{\sqrt{16\omega^2+9a^2}}{2\omega^5(a^2+\omega^2)}\sin(\omega t+\phi_2)$ $+\frac{1}{a^2(a^2+\omega^2)^2}\epsilon^{-at}$; $\phi_1 = \tan^{-1}\left(\frac{a}{\omega}\right)$, $\phi_2 = \tan^{-1}\left(\frac{4\omega}{3a}\right) - 2\tan^{-1}\left(\frac{\omega}{a}\right)$
58	$\frac{1}{s^2+2as+b^2}$	$\frac{1}{\sqrt{b^2-a^2}}\epsilon^{-at}\sin\sqrt{b^2-a^2}\,t$

NO.	F(s)	f(t)
59	$\frac{1}{(s+a)^2+\omega^2}$	$\frac{1}{\omega}\epsilon^{-at}\sin\omega t$
60	$\frac{1}{s(s^2+2as+b^2)}$	$\frac{1}{b^2}\left[1-\frac{b}{\sqrt{b^2-a^2}}\epsilon^{-at}\sin(\sqrt{b^2-a^2}\,t+\phi)\right]$; $\phi=\tan^{-1}\left(\frac{\sqrt{b^2-a^2}}{a}\right)$
61	$\frac{1}{s[(s+a)^2+\omega^2]}$	$\frac{1}{(a^2+\omega^2)}\left[1-\frac{\sqrt{a^2+\omega^2}}{\omega}\epsilon^{-at}\sin(\omega t+\phi)\right]$; $\phi=\tan^{-1}\left(\frac{\omega}{a}\right)$
62	$\frac{1}{s^2[(s+a)^2+\omega^2]}$	$\frac{1}{(a^2+\omega^2)}\left[t-\frac{2a}{a^2+\omega^2}+\frac{1}{\omega}\epsilon^{-at}\sin(\omega t+\phi)\right]$; $\phi=2\tan^{-1}\left(\frac{\omega}{a}\right)$
63	$\frac{1}{(s+b)[(s+a)^2+\omega^2]}$	$\frac{1}{[(b-a)^2+\omega^2]}\left[\epsilon^{-bt}+\frac{\sqrt{(b-a)^2+\omega^2}}{\omega}\epsilon^{-at}\sin(\omega t-\phi)\right]$; $\phi=\tan^{-1}\left(\frac{\omega}{b-a}\right)$
64	$\frac{1}{s(s+b)[(s+a)^2+\omega^2]}$	$\frac{1}{b(a^2+\omega^2)}-\frac{1}{b[(a-b)^2+\omega^2]}\epsilon^{-bt}-\frac{1}{\omega\sqrt{(a^2+\omega^2)[(a-b)^2+\omega^2]}}\epsilon^{-at}\sin(\omega t+\phi)$ $\phi=\tan^{-1}\left(\frac{\omega}{a}\right)+\tan^{-1}\left(\frac{\omega}{a-b}\right)$
65	$\frac{1}{s^2(s+b)[(s+a)^2+\omega^2]}$	$\frac{1}{b(a^2+\omega^2)}\left(t-\frac{1}{b}-\frac{2a}{a^2+\omega^2}\right)+\frac{1}{b^2[(b-a)^2+\omega^2]}\epsilon^{-bt}$ $+\frac{1}{\omega(a^2+\omega^2)\sqrt{(b-a)^2+\omega^2}}\epsilon^{-at}\sin(\omega t+\phi)$; $\phi=2\tan^{-1}\left(\frac{\omega}{a}\right)-\tan^{-1}\left(\frac{\omega}{b-a}\right)$
66	$\frac{1}{(s+b)(s+c)[(s+a)^2+\omega^2]}$	$\frac{1}{(c-b)[(a-b)^2+\omega^2]}\epsilon^{-bt}+\frac{1}{(b-c)[(a-c)^2+\omega^2]}\epsilon^{-ct}$ $+\frac{1}{\omega\sqrt{[(a-c)^2+\omega^2][(a-b)^2+\omega^2]}}\epsilon^{-at}\cos(\omega t+\phi)$ $\phi=\tan^{-1}\left(\frac{\omega}{a-c}\right)-\tan^{-1}\left(\frac{a-b}{\omega}\right)$
67	$\frac{1}{(s+b)^2[(s+a)^2+\omega^2]}$	$\frac{1}{[(a-b)^2+\omega^2]}\left[t\epsilon^{-bt}+\frac{2(b-a)}{[(a-b)^2+\omega^2]}\epsilon^{-bt}+\frac{1}{\omega}\epsilon^{-at}\sin(\omega t-\phi)\right]$; $\phi=2\tan^{-1}\left(\frac{\omega}{b-a}\right)$
68	$\frac{1}{s(s+b)^2[(s+a)^2+\omega^2]}$	$\frac{1}{[(a-b)^2+\omega^2]}\left[\frac{[(a-b)^2+\omega^2]}{b^2(a^2+\omega^2)}-\frac{1}{b}t\epsilon^{-bt}-\left(\frac{1}{b^2}-\frac{2(a-b)}{b[(a-b)^2+\omega^2]}\right)\epsilon^{-bt}\right.$ $\left.-\frac{1}{\omega\sqrt{a^2+\omega^2}}\epsilon^{-at}\sin(\omega t+\phi)\right]$; $\phi=2\tan^{-1}\left(\frac{b-a}{\omega}\right)+\tan^{-1}\left(\frac{\omega}{a}\right)$
69	$\frac{1}{(s^2+b^2)[(s+a)^2+\omega^2]}$	$\frac{1}{\omega b\sqrt{4a^2b^2+(a^2+\omega^2-b^2)^2}}\left[-\omega\sin(bt+\phi_1)+b\epsilon^{-at}\sin(\omega t+\phi_2)\right]$ $\phi_1=\tan^{-1}\left(\frac{2ab}{b^2-a^2-\omega^2}\right)$, $\phi_2=\tan^{-1}\left[\frac{2a\omega}{(a^2-\omega^2+b^2)}\right]$
70	$\frac{1}{s(s^2+b^2)[(s+a)^2+\omega^2]}$	$\frac{1}{b^2(a^2+\omega^2)}+\frac{1}{\omega\sqrt{(a^2+\omega^2)[(a^2+b^2-\omega^2)^2+4a^2\omega^2]}}\epsilon^{-at}\sin(\omega t-\phi_1)-\frac{\sin(bt+\phi_2)}{b^2\sqrt{(a^2+\omega^2-b^2)^2+4a^2b^2}}$ $\phi_1=\tan^{-1}\left(\frac{a}{\omega}\right)+\tan^{-1}\left(\frac{a^2-\omega^2+b^2}{2a\omega}\right)$; $\phi_2=\tan^{-1}\left(\frac{a^2+\omega^2-b^2}{2ab}\right)$

NO.	F(s)	f(t)
71	$\frac{1}{(s+c)(s^2+b^2)[(s+a)^2+\omega^2]}$	$\frac{1}{(c^2+b^2)[(a-c)^2+\omega^2]}\epsilon^{-ct}+\frac{1}{\sqrt{[4a^2b^2+(a^2+\omega^2-b^2)^2]}}\left[\frac{1}{\omega\sqrt{(c-a)^2+\omega^2}}\epsilon^{-at}\sin(\omega t+\phi_1)-\frac{1}{b\sqrt{(c^2+b^2)}}\sin(bt+\phi_2)\right]$ $\phi_1=\tan^{-1}\left(\frac{c-a}{\omega}\right)-\tan^{-1}\left(\frac{a^2-\omega^2+b^2}{2a\omega}\right);\ \phi_2=\tan^{-1}\left(\frac{c}{b}\right)+\tan^{-1}\left(\frac{a^2+\omega^2-b^2}{2ab}\right)$
72	$\frac{1}{[(s+a)^2+\omega^2]^2}$	$\frac{1}{2\omega^3}\epsilon^{-at}[\sin\omega t-\omega t\cos\omega t]$
73	$\frac{1}{s^2-a^2}$	$\frac{1}{a}\sinh at$
74	$\frac{1}{s^2(s^2-a^2)}$	$\frac{1}{a^3}\sinh at-\frac{1}{a^2}t$
75	$\frac{1}{s^3(s^2-a^2)}$	$\frac{1}{a^4}(\cosh at-1)-\frac{1}{2a^2}t^2$
76	$\frac{1}{s^3+a^3}$	$\frac{1}{3a^2}\left[\epsilon^{-at}-\epsilon^{\frac{a}{2}t}\left(\cos\frac{\sqrt{3}}{2}at-\sqrt{3}\sin\frac{\sqrt{3}}{2}at\right)\right]$
77	$\frac{1}{s^4+4a^4}$	$\frac{1}{4a^3}(\sin at\cosh at-\cos at\sinh at)$
78	$\frac{1}{s^4-a^4}$	$\frac{1}{2a^3}(\sinh at-\sin at)$
79	$\frac{1}{[(s+a)^2-\omega^2]}$	$\frac{1}{\omega}\epsilon^{-at}\sinh\omega t$
80	$\frac{1}{s\sqrt{s+1}}$	$\operatorname{erf}(\sqrt{t})$; $\operatorname{erf}(y)\triangleq$ the error function $=\frac{2}{\sqrt{\pi}}\int_0^y\epsilon^{-u^2}du$
81	$\frac{1}{\sqrt{s^2+a^2}}$	$J_0(at)$; Bessel function of 1st kind, zero order.
82	$\frac{1}{\sqrt{s^2+a^2}+s}$	$\frac{J_1(at)}{at}$; J_1 is the Bessel function of 1st kind, 1st order.
83	$\frac{1}{[\sqrt{s^2+a^2}+s]^N}$	$\frac{N}{a^N}\frac{J_N(at)}{t}$; $N=1,2,3,\cdots$ J_N is the Bessel function of 1st kind, Nth order.
84	$\frac{1}{s[\sqrt{s^2+a^2}+s]^N}$	$\frac{N}{a^N}\int_0^t\frac{J_N(au)}{u}du$; $N=1,2,3,\cdots$ J_N is the Bessel function of 1st kind, Nth order.
85	$\frac{1}{\sqrt{s^2+a^2}(\sqrt{s^2+a^2}+s)}$	$\frac{1}{a}J_1(at)$; J_1 is the Bessel function of 1st kind, 1st order.
86	$\frac{1}{\sqrt{s^2+a^2}[\sqrt{s^2+a^2}+s]^N}$	$\frac{1}{a^N}J_N(at)$; $N=1,2,3,\cdots$ J_N is the Bessel function of 1st kind, Nth order.
87	$\frac{1}{\sqrt{(s^2-a^2)}}$	$I_0(at)$; I_0 is modified Bessel function of 1st kind, zero order.

NO.	F(s)	f(t)
88	$\frac{1}{\sqrt{s^2-1}}$	$I_0(t)$; I_0 is modified Bessel function of 1st kind, zero order.
89	$\frac{1}{\sqrt{s}\,(s-1)}$	$\epsilon^{t}\,\mathrm{erf}(\sqrt{t})$; Where $\mathrm{erf}(y)=\frac{2}{\sqrt{\pi}}\int_0^y \epsilon^{-u^2}du$.
90	$\frac{1}{1+\sqrt{s}}$	$\frac{1}{\sqrt{\pi t}}-\epsilon^{t}+\epsilon^{t}\mathrm{erf}(\sqrt{t})$; Where $\mathrm{erf}(y)=\frac{2}{\sqrt{\pi}}\int_0^y \epsilon^{-u^2}du$.
91	$\frac{1}{\sqrt{s^2-a^2}(s+\sqrt{s^2-a^2})^N}$	$\frac{1}{a^N}I_N(at)$; I_N is modified Bessel function of 1st kind, Nth order.
92	$\frac{s}{(s+a)(s+b)}$	$\frac{1}{(a-b)}\left[a\epsilon^{-at}-b\epsilon^{-bt}\right]$
93	$\frac{s}{(s-a)(s-b)}$	$\frac{1}{(a-b)}\left[a\epsilon^{at}-b\epsilon^{bt}\right]$
94	$\frac{s}{(s+a)(s+b)(s+c)}$	$\frac{-a}{(b-a)(c-a)}\epsilon^{-at}-\frac{b}{(a-b)(c-b)}\epsilon^{-bt}-\frac{c}{(a-c)(b-c)}\epsilon^{-ct}$
95	$\frac{s}{(s+a)^2}$	$(1-at)\epsilon^{-at}$
96	$\frac{s}{(s+a)^3}$	$(1-\frac{a}{2}t)t\epsilon^{-at}$
97	$\frac{s}{(s+a)(s+b)^2}$	$\frac{a}{(b-a)^2}\left[\epsilon^{-bt}-\epsilon^{-at}+\frac{b}{a}(b-a)t\epsilon^{-bt}\right]$
98	$\frac{s}{(s+a)^2(s+b)^2}$	$\frac{1}{(a-b)^2}\left[\left(\frac{a+b}{a-b}\right)\left(\epsilon^{-bt}-\epsilon^{-at}\right)-t(a\epsilon^{-at}+b\epsilon^{-bt})\right]$
99	$\frac{s}{s^2+\omega^2}$	$\cos\omega t$
100	$\frac{s}{(s+a)(s^2+\omega^2)}$	$\frac{1}{a^2+\omega^2}\left[\sqrt{a^2+\omega^2}\sin(\omega t+\phi)-a\epsilon^{-at}\right]$; $\phi=\frac{\pi}{2}-\tan^{-1}\left(\frac{\omega}{a}\right)$
101	$\frac{s}{(s+a)^2(s^2+\omega^2)}$	$\frac{\omega^2-a^2}{(a^2+\omega^2)^2}\epsilon^{-at}-\frac{a}{a^2+\omega^2}t\epsilon^{-at}+\frac{1}{a^2+\omega^2}\sin(\omega t+\phi)$; $\phi=\tan^{-1}\left(\frac{a^2-\omega^2}{2a\omega}\right)$
102	$\frac{s}{(s+a)(s+b)(s^2+\omega^2)}$	$\frac{a}{(a^2+\omega^2)(a-b)}\epsilon^{-at}-\frac{b}{(b^2+\omega^2)(a-b)}\epsilon^{-bt}+\frac{1}{\sqrt{(ab-\omega^2)^2+(a+b)^2\omega^2}}\sin(\omega t+\phi)$ $\phi=\tan^{-1}\frac{ab-\omega^2}{\omega(a+b)}$
103	$\frac{s}{(s^2+a^2)(s^2+\omega^2)}$	$\frac{1}{\omega^2-a^2}\left[\cos at-\cos\omega t\right]$
104	$\frac{s}{(s^2+\omega^2)^2}$	$\frac{1}{2\omega}t\sin\omega t$
105	$\frac{s}{s^2+2as+b^2}$	$\frac{1}{2\sqrt{a^2-b^2}}\left[(a+\sqrt{a^2-b^2})\epsilon^{-(a+\sqrt{a^2-b^2})t}-(a-\sqrt{a^2-b^2})\epsilon^{-(a-\sqrt{a^2-b^2})t}\right]$

NO.	F(s)	f(t)
106	$\frac{s}{[(s+a)^2+\omega^2]}$	$\frac{\sqrt{a^2+\omega^2}}{\omega}\epsilon^{-at}\sin(\omega t+\phi)$; $\phi=\tan^{-1}\left(\frac{\omega}{-a}\right)$
107	$\frac{s}{(s+c)[(s+a)^2+\omega^2]}$	$\frac{-c}{(a-c)^2+\omega^2}\epsilon^{-ct}+\frac{1}{\omega}\sqrt{\frac{a^2+\omega^2}{(c-a)^2+\omega^2}}\epsilon^{-at}\sin(\omega t+\phi)$; $\phi=\tan^{-1}\left(\frac{\omega}{-a}\right)-\tan^{-1}\left(\frac{\omega}{c-a}\right)$
108	$\frac{s}{(s^2+c^2)[(s+a)^2+\omega^2]}$	$\frac{1}{\sqrt{(a^2+\omega^2-c^2)^2+4c^2a^2}}\left[\sin(ct+\phi_1)+\frac{\sqrt{a^2+\omega^2}}{\omega}\epsilon^{-at}\sin(\omega t+\phi_2)\right]$ $\phi_1=\frac{\pi}{2}-\tan^{-1}\left(\frac{2ac}{a^2+\omega^2-c^2}\right)$; $\phi_2=\tan^{-1}\left(\frac{\omega}{-a}\right)-\tan^{-1}\left(\frac{-2a\omega}{c^2+a^2-\omega^2}\right)$
109	$\frac{s}{[(s+a)^2+\omega^2]^2}$	$\frac{1}{2\omega^3}\left[a\omega t\cos\omega t-(a-\omega^2 t)\sin\omega t\right]\epsilon^{-at}$
110	$\frac{s}{[s^2+(a+b)^2][s^2+(a-b)^2]}$	$\frac{1}{2ab}\sin(at)\sin(bt)$
111	$\frac{s}{s^2-\omega^2}$	$\cosh\omega t$
112	$\frac{s}{s^3+a^3}$	$\frac{1}{3a}\left[-\epsilon^{-at}+\epsilon^{\frac{1}{2}at}\left(\cos\frac{\sqrt{3}}{2}at+\sqrt{3}\sin\frac{\sqrt{3}}{2}at\right)\right]$
113	$\frac{s}{s^4-\omega^4}$	$\frac{1}{2\omega^2}\left[\cosh\omega t-\cos\omega t\right]$
114	$\frac{s}{s^4+4a^4}$	$\frac{1}{2a^2}\left[\sin(at)\sinh(at)\right]$
115	$\frac{s}{(s-a)^{3/2}}$	$\frac{(1+2at)}{\sqrt{\pi t}}\epsilon^{at}$
116	$\frac{s+a}{s(s+b)}$	$\frac{a}{b}-\frac{(a-b)}{b}\epsilon^{-bt}$
117	$\frac{s+a}{s^2(s+b)}$	$\frac{a}{b}t+\frac{b-a}{b^2}(1-\epsilon^{-bt})$
118	$\frac{s+a}{s^3(s+b)}$	$\frac{a}{2b}t^2+\left(\frac{b-a}{b^2}\right)\left[t+\frac{1}{b}\epsilon^{-bt}-\frac{1}{b}\right]$
119	$\frac{s+a}{(s+b)(s+c)}$	$\frac{1}{(c-b)}\left[(a-b)\epsilon^{-bt}-(a-c)\epsilon^{-ct}\right]$
120	$\frac{s+a}{s(s+b)(s+c)}$	$\frac{a}{bc}+\frac{a-b}{b(b-c)}\epsilon^{-bt}+\frac{a-c}{c(c-b)}\epsilon^{-ct}$
121	$\frac{s+a}{s^2(s+b)(s+c)}$	$\frac{1}{bc}(1+at)-\frac{(b+c)a}{b^2c^2}+\frac{1}{c-b}\left[\frac{(a-b)}{b^2}\epsilon^{-bt}-\frac{(a-c)}{c^2}\epsilon^{-ct}\right]$
122	$\frac{s+a}{(s+b)(s+c)(s+d)}$	$\frac{(a-b)}{(c-b)(d-b)}\epsilon^{-bt}+\frac{(a-c)}{(b-c)(d-c)}\epsilon^{-ct}+\frac{(a-d)}{(b-d)(c-d)}\epsilon^{-dt}$
123	$\frac{s+a}{s(s+b)(s+c)(s+d)}$	$\frac{a}{bcd}+\frac{(b-a)}{b(c-b)(d-b)}\epsilon^{-bt}+\frac{(c-a)}{c(b-c)(d-c)}\epsilon^{-ct}+\frac{(d-a)}{d(b-d)(c-d)}\epsilon^{-dt}$

NO.	F(s)	f(t)
124	$\frac{s+a}{s^2(s+b)(s+c)(s+d)}$	$\frac{1}{bcd}(1+at)-\frac{a(bc+cd+db)}{b^2c^2d^2}+\frac{(a-b)}{b^2(c-b)(d-b)}\epsilon^{-bt}+\frac{(a-c)}{c^2(b-c)(d-c)}\epsilon^{-ct}$ $+\frac{(a-d)}{d^2(b-d)(c-d)}\epsilon^{-dt}$
125	$\frac{s+a}{(s+b)^2}$	$\left[1+(a-b)t\right]\epsilon^{-bt}$
126	$\frac{s+a}{s(s+b)^2}$	$\frac{a}{b^2}+\left[\left(1-\frac{a}{b}\right)t-\frac{a}{b^2}\right]\epsilon^{-bt}$
127	$\frac{s+a}{s^2(s+b)^2}$	$\frac{1}{b^2}\left\{\left(1+at-\frac{2a}{b}\right)-\left(1-\frac{2a}{b}+[b-a]t\right)\epsilon^{-bt}\right\}$
128	$\frac{s+a}{(s+b)(s+c)^2}$	$\frac{(a-b)}{(b-c)^2}\epsilon^{-bt}+\left[\frac{a-c}{b-c}t+\frac{b-a}{(b-c)^2}\right]\epsilon^{-ct}$
129	$\frac{s+a}{s(s+b)(s+c)^2}$	$\frac{a}{bc^2}+\frac{(b-a)}{b(c-b)^2}\epsilon^{-bt}+\left[\frac{(a-c)}{c(c-b)}t-\frac{c^2-a(2c-b)}{c^2(c-b)^2}\right]\epsilon^{-ct}$
130	$\frac{s+a}{s^2(s+b)(s+c)^2}$	$\frac{a}{bc^2}\left[\left(\frac{1}{a}-\frac{1}{b}-\frac{2}{c}\right)+t\right]-\frac{(b-a)}{b^2(c-b)^2}\epsilon^{-bt}-\left[\frac{c-a}{c^2(b-c)}t+\frac{(2a-c)(2c-b)-ac}{c^3(c-b)^2}\right]\epsilon^{-ct}$
131	$\frac{s+a}{(s+b)^2(s+c)^2}$	$\left[\frac{(a-c)}{(b-c)^2}t+\frac{b+c-2a}{(b-c)^3}\right]\epsilon^{-ct}+\left[\frac{(a-b)}{(c-b)^2}t+\frac{b+c-2a}{(c-b)^3}\right]\epsilon^{-bt}$
132	$\frac{s+a}{s(s+b)^2(s+c)^2}$	$\frac{a}{b^2c^2}+\left[\frac{(c-a)}{c(b-c)^2}t+\frac{3ac-ab-2c^2}{c^2(b-c)^3}\right]\epsilon^{-ct}+\left[\frac{(b-a)}{b(c-b)^2}t+\frac{3ab-ac-2b^2}{b^2(c-b)^3}\right]\epsilon^{-bt}$
133	$\frac{s+a}{s^2(s+b)^2(s+c)^2}$	$\left[\frac{1}{b^2c^2}(1+at)-\frac{2a(b+c)}{b^3c^3}\right]+\left[\frac{(a-b)}{b^2(c-b)^2}t+\frac{2a(c-2b)+b(3b-c)}{b^3(c-b)^3}\right]\epsilon^{-bt}$ $+\left[\frac{(a-c)}{c^2(b-c)^2}t+\frac{2a(b-2c)+c(3c-b)}{c^3(b-c)^3}\right]\epsilon^{-ct}$
134	$\frac{s+a}{(s+b)(s+c)(s+d)^2}$	$\frac{(a-b)}{(c-b)(d-b)^2}\epsilon^{-bt}+\frac{(a-c)}{(b-c)(d-c)^2}\epsilon^{-ct}+\left[\frac{(a-d)}{(d-c)(d-b)}t+\frac{a(2d-b-c)-d^2+bc}{(d-b)^2(d-c)^2}\right]\epsilon^{-dt}$
135	$\frac{s+a}{s(s+b)(s+c)(s+d)^2}$	$\frac{a}{bcd^2}-\frac{(a-c)}{c(b-c)(d-c)^2}\epsilon^{-ct}-\frac{(a-b)}{b(c-b)(d-b)^2}\epsilon^{-bt}$ $+\left[\frac{(d-a)}{d(d-c)(d-b)}t-\frac{a(d-c)(d-b)+d(a-d)(2d-b-c)}{d^2(d-c)^2(d-b)^2}\right]\epsilon^{-dt}$
136	$\frac{s+a}{(s+b)(s+c)^2(s+d)^2}$	$\frac{(a-b)}{(b-c)^2(b-d)^2}\epsilon^{-bt}+\left[\frac{(c-2a)(b-c)+(db-c^2)-a(d-c)}{(c-b)^2(d-c)^3}+\frac{(a-c)}{(b-c)(c-d)^2}t\right]\epsilon^{-ct}$ $+\left[\frac{(d-2a)(b-d)+(bc-d^2)-a(c-d)}{(d-b)^2(c-d)^3}+\frac{(a-d)}{(b-d)(c-d)^2}t\right]\epsilon^{-dt}$
137	$\frac{s+a}{s^2+\omega^2}$	$\frac{\sqrt{a^2+\omega^2}}{\omega}\sin(\omega t+\phi)$; $\phi=\tan^{-1}\left(\frac{\omega}{a}\right)$
138	$\frac{s+a}{s(s^2+\omega^2)}$	$\frac{a}{\omega^2}-\frac{\sqrt{a^2+\omega^2}}{\omega^2}\cos(\omega t+\phi)$; $\phi=\tan^{-1}\left(\frac{\omega}{a}\right)$

NO.	F(s)	f(t)
139	$\frac{s+a}{s^2(s^2+\omega^2)}$	$\frac{a}{\omega^2}t+\frac{1}{\omega^2}-\frac{\sqrt{a^2+\omega^2}}{\omega^3}\sin(\omega t+\phi);\quad \phi=\tan^{-1}\left(\frac{\omega}{a}\right)$
140	$\frac{s+a}{(s+b)(s^2+\omega^2)}$	$\frac{(a-b)}{b^2+\omega^2}\epsilon^{-bt}+\frac{1}{\omega}\sqrt{\frac{a^2+\omega^2}{b^2+\omega^2}}\sin(\omega t+\phi);\quad \phi=\tan^{-1}\left(\frac{\omega}{a}\right)-\tan^{-1}\left(\frac{\omega}{b}\right)$
141	$\frac{s+a}{s(s+b)(s^2+\omega^2)}$	$\frac{a}{b\omega^2}+\frac{b-a}{b(b^2+\omega^2)}\epsilon^{-bt}-\frac{1}{\omega^2}\sqrt{\frac{a^2+\omega^2}{b^2+\omega^2}}\cos(\omega t+\phi);\quad \phi=\tan^{-1}\left(\frac{\omega}{a}\right)-\tan^{-1}\left(\frac{\omega}{b}\right)$
142	$\frac{s+a}{s^2(s+b)(s^2+\omega^2)}$	$\frac{1}{b\omega^2}\left[1-\frac{a}{b}+at\right]+\frac{(a-b)}{b^2(b^2+\omega^2)}\epsilon^{-bt}+\frac{1}{\omega^3}\sqrt{\frac{a^2+\omega^2}{b^2+\omega^2}}\cos(\omega t+\phi)$ $\phi=\tan^{-1}\left(\frac{b}{\omega}\right)+\tan^{-1}\left(\frac{\omega}{a}\right)$
143	$\frac{s+a}{(s+b)^2(s^2+\omega^2)}$	$\left[\frac{2ab-b^2+\omega^2}{(b^2+\omega^2)^2}-\frac{(b-a)}{b^2+\omega^2}t\right]\epsilon^{-bt}+\frac{\sqrt{\omega^2+a^2}}{\omega(b^2+\omega^2)}\sin(\omega t+\phi)$ $\phi=\tan^{-1}\left(\frac{\omega}{a}\right)-2\tan^{-1}\left(\frac{\omega}{b}\right)$
144	$\frac{s+a}{s(s+b)^2(s^2+\omega^2)}$	$\frac{a}{b^2\omega^2}+\left[\frac{2b^2(b-a)-a(b^2+\omega^2)}{b^2(b^2+\omega^2)^2}+\frac{(b-a)}{b(b^2+\omega^2)}t\right]\epsilon^{-bt}-\frac{\sqrt{a^2+\omega^2}}{\omega^2(b^2+\omega^2)}\cos(\omega t+\phi)$ $\phi=\tan^{-1}\left(\frac{\omega}{a}\right)-2\tan^{-1}\left(\frac{\omega}{b}\right)$
145	$\frac{s+a}{s^2(s+b)^2(s^2+\omega^2)}$	$\frac{1}{b^2\omega^2}\left[1-\frac{2a}{b}+at\right]+\left[\frac{(b^2+\omega^2)(2a-b)+2b^2(a-b)}{b^3(b^2+\omega^2)^2}+\frac{(a-b)}{b^2(b^2+\omega^2)}t\right]\epsilon^{-bt}$ $+\frac{\sqrt{a^2+\omega^2}}{\omega^3(b^2+\omega^2)}\sin(\omega t+\phi);\quad \phi=\tan^{-1}\left(\frac{\omega}{a}\right)+2\tan^{-1}\left(\frac{b}{\omega}\right)$
146	$\frac{s+a}{(s+b)(s+c)(s^2+\omega^2)}$	$\frac{(a-b)}{(c-b)(b^2+\omega^2)}\epsilon^{-bt}+\frac{(a-c)}{(b-c)(c^2+\omega^2)}\epsilon^{-ct}+\frac{1}{\omega}\sqrt{\frac{a^2+\omega^2}{(b^2+\omega^2)(\omega^2+c^2)}}\sin(\omega t+\phi)$ $\phi=\tan^{-1}\left(\frac{c}{\omega}\right)-\tan^{-1}\left(\frac{a}{\omega}\right)-\tan^{-1}\left(\frac{\omega}{b}\right)$
147	$\frac{s+a}{s(s+b)(s+c)(s^2+\omega^2)}$	$\frac{a}{bc\omega^2}+\frac{(b-a)}{b(c-b)(b^2+\omega^2)}\epsilon^{-bt}+\frac{(c-a)}{c(b-c)(c^2+\omega^2)}\epsilon^{-ct}+\frac{1}{\omega^2}\sqrt{\frac{a^2+\omega^2}{\omega^2(b+c)^2+(bc-\omega^2)^2}}\sin(\omega t-\phi)$ $\phi=\tan^{-1}\left(\frac{\omega}{b}\right)+\tan^{-1}\left(\frac{\omega}{c}\right)+\tan^{-1}\left(\frac{a}{\omega}\right)$
148	$\frac{s+a}{s^2(s+b)(s+c)(s^2+\omega^2)}$	$\frac{1}{bc\omega^2}\left(1-\frac{a}{c}-\frac{a}{b}+at\right)+\frac{(a-b)}{b^2(c-b)(b^2+\omega^2)}\epsilon^{-bt}+\frac{(a-c)}{c^2(b-c)(c^2+\omega^2)}\epsilon^{-ct}$ $+\frac{1}{\omega^3}\sqrt{\frac{a^2+\omega^2}{\omega^2(b+c)^2+(bc-\omega^2)^2}}\cos(\omega t+\phi)$ $\phi=\tan^{-1}\left(\frac{c}{\omega}\right)-\tan^{-1}\left(\frac{\omega}{b}\right)+\tan^{-1}\left(\frac{\omega}{a}\right)$

NO.	F(s)	f(t)
149	$\dfrac{s+a}{(s+b)(s+c)^2(s^2+\omega^2)}$	$\dfrac{(a-b)}{(\omega^2+b^2)(c-b)^2}\epsilon^{-bt}+\left[\dfrac{c^2(c-a)+\omega^2(b-a)+c(b-c)(2a-c)}{(c^2+\omega^2)^2(b-c)^2}+\dfrac{(a-c)}{(b-c)(c^2+\omega^2)}t\right]\epsilon^{-ct}$ $+\dfrac{1}{\omega}\sqrt{\dfrac{a^2+\omega^2}{(\omega^2+b^2)(\omega^2+c^2)^2}}\sin(\omega t+\phi)$ $\phi=\tan^{-1}\left(\dfrac{b}{\omega}\right)-\tan^{-1}\left(\dfrac{a}{\omega}\right)-2\tan^{-1}\left(\dfrac{\omega}{c}\right)$
150	$\dfrac{s+a}{(s+b)^2(s+c)^2(s^2+\omega^2)}$	$\left[\dfrac{(a-b)}{(c-b)^2(b^2+\omega^2)}t+\dfrac{2b(a-b)}{(c-b)^2(b^2+\omega^2)^2}+\dfrac{b+c-2a}{(c-b)^3(b^2+\omega^2)}\right]\epsilon^{-bt}+\dfrac{\sqrt{a^2+\omega^2}}{\omega(b^2+\omega^2)(c^2+\omega^2)}\sin(\omega t+\phi)$ $+\left[\dfrac{(a-c)}{(c-b)^2(c^2+\omega^2)}t+\dfrac{2c(a-c)}{(b-c)^2(c^2+\omega^2)^2}+\dfrac{b+c-2a}{(b-c)^3(c^2+\omega^2)}\right]\epsilon^{-ct}$ $\phi=\tan^{-1}\left(\dfrac{\omega}{a}\right)+2\left[\tan^{-1}\left(\dfrac{c}{\omega}\right)+\tan^{-1}\left(\dfrac{b}{\omega}\right)\right]$
151	$\dfrac{s+a}{(s^2+b^2)(s^2+\omega^2)}$	$\dfrac{1}{(b^2-\omega^2)}\left[\dfrac{\sqrt{\omega^2+a^2}}{\omega}\cos(\omega t-\phi_1)-\dfrac{\sqrt{b^2+a^2}}{b}\cos(bt-\phi_2)\right]$ $\phi_1=\tan^{-1}\left(\dfrac{a}{\omega}\right)\ ,\quad \phi_2=\tan^{-1}\left(\dfrac{a}{b}\right)$
152	$\dfrac{s+a}{(s^2+\omega^2)^2}$	$\dfrac{1}{2\omega^3}\left[(a+\omega^2t)\sin\omega t-a\omega t\ \cos\omega t\right]$
153	$\dfrac{s+a}{s(s^2+\omega^2)^2}$	$\dfrac{1}{2\omega^3}\left[\dfrac{2a}{\omega}+(1-at)\sin\omega t-\dfrac{1}{\omega}(2a+\omega^2t)\cos\omega t\right]$
154	$\dfrac{s+a}{s^2(s^2+\omega^2)^2}$	$\dfrac{1}{2\omega^4}\left[2+2at-\dfrac{1}{\omega}\sqrt{4\omega^2+9a^2}\sin(\omega t+\phi_1)+\sqrt{a^2+\omega^2}\ t\ \cos(\omega t+\phi_2)\right]$ $\phi_1=\tan^{-1}\left(\dfrac{2\omega}{3a}\right)\ ,\quad \phi_2=\tan^{-1}\left(\dfrac{\omega}{a}\right)$
155	$\dfrac{s+a}{(s+b)(s^2+\omega^2)^2}$	$\dfrac{(a-b)}{(\omega^2+b^2)^2}\epsilon^{-bt}-\dfrac{1}{2\omega^2}\sqrt{\dfrac{a^2+\omega^2}{\omega^2+b^2}}\,t\ \sin(\omega t+\phi_1)+\dfrac{\sqrt{(\omega^2-ba)^2+4\omega^2a^2}}{2\omega^3(\omega^2+b^2)}\cos(\omega t+\phi_2)$ $\phi_1=\tan^{-1}\left(\dfrac{\omega}{a}\right)+\tan^{-1}\left(\dfrac{b}{\omega}\right),\quad \phi_2=\tan^{-1}\left(\dfrac{\omega^2-ba}{2\omega a}\right)-2\tan^{-1}\left(\dfrac{\omega}{b}\right)$
156	$\dfrac{s+a}{s(s+b)(s^2+\omega^2)^2}$	$\dfrac{a}{b\omega^4}+\dfrac{(b-a)}{b(\omega^2+b^2)^2}\epsilon^{-bt}+\dfrac{1}{2\omega^3}\sqrt{\dfrac{\omega^2+a^2}{\omega^2+b^2}}\,t\ \cos(\omega t+\phi_1)-\dfrac{\sqrt{\omega^2(3a+b)^2+4(ba-\omega^2)^2}}{2\omega^4(\omega^2+b^2)}\cos(\omega t+\phi_2)$ $\phi_1=\tan^{-1}\left(\dfrac{\omega}{a}\right)+\tan^{-1}\left(\dfrac{b}{\omega}\right),\quad \phi_2=\tan^{-1}\left[\dfrac{\omega(3a+b)}{2(ba-\omega^2)}\right]-2\tan^{-1}\left(\dfrac{\omega}{b}\right)$
157	$\dfrac{s+a}{s^2(s+b)(s^2+\omega^2)^2}$	$\dfrac{1}{b\omega^4}\left(1-\dfrac{a}{b}+at\right)+\dfrac{(a-b)}{b^2(\omega^2+b^2)^2}\epsilon^{-bt}+\dfrac{1}{2\omega^4}\sqrt{\dfrac{\omega^2+a^2}{\omega^2+b^2}}\,t\ \sin(\omega t+\phi_1)$ $+\dfrac{\sqrt{4\omega^2(2a+b)^2+9(ab-\omega^2)^2}}{2\omega^5(\omega^2+b^2)}\sin(\omega t+\phi_2)$ $\phi_1=\tan^{-1}\left(\dfrac{\omega}{a}\right)+\tan^{-1}\left(\dfrac{b}{\omega}\right),\quad \phi_2=\tan^{-1}\left[\dfrac{2\omega(2a+b)}{3(ab-\omega^2)}\right]-2\tan^{-1}\left(\dfrac{\omega}{b}\right)$

NO.	F(s)	f(t)
158	$\frac{s\sin\phi+\omega\cos\phi}{(s^2+\omega^2)}$	$\sin(\omega t+\phi)$
159	$\frac{s\cos\phi-\omega\sin\phi}{(s^2+\omega^2)}$	$\cos(\omega t+\phi)$
160	$\frac{s+a}{(s+b)^2+\omega^2}$	$\frac{1}{\omega}\sqrt{(a-b)^2+\omega^2}\,\epsilon^{-bt}\sin(\omega t+\phi)\,;\quad \phi=\tan^{-1}\left(\frac{\omega}{a-b}\right)$
161	$\frac{(s+b)\cos\phi\pm\omega\sin\phi}{(s+b)^2+\omega^2}$	$\epsilon^{-bt}\cos(\omega t\mp\phi)$
162	$\frac{\omega\cos\phi\pm(s+b)\sin\phi}{(s+b)^2+\omega^2}$	$\epsilon^{-bt}\sin(\omega t\pm\phi)$
163	$\frac{s+a}{(s+a)^2+\omega^2}$	$\epsilon^{-at}\cos\omega t$ $= e^{-at}\sin(\omega t+\phi)$
164	$\frac{s+a}{s\left[(s+b)^2+\omega^2\right]}$	$\frac{a}{b^2+\omega^2}-\frac{1}{\omega}\sqrt{\frac{(a-b)^2+\omega^2}{b^2+\omega^2}}\,\epsilon^{-bt}\sin(\omega t+\phi)\,;\quad \phi=\tan^{-1}\left(\frac{\omega}{b}\right)+\tan^{-1}\left(\frac{\omega}{a-b}\right)$
165	$\frac{s+a}{s^2\left[(s+b)^2+\omega^2\right]}$	$\frac{1}{b^2+\omega^2}[1+at]-\frac{2ab}{(b^2+\omega^2)^2}+\frac{\sqrt{(a-b)^2+\omega^2}}{\omega(b^2+\omega^2)}\,\epsilon^{-bt}\sin(\omega t+\phi)$ $\phi=\tan^{-1}\left(\frac{\omega}{a-b}\right)+2\tan^{-1}\left(\frac{\omega}{b}\right)$
166	$\frac{s+a}{(s+c)\left[(s+b)^2+\omega^2\right]}$	$\frac{(a-c)}{(c-b)^2+\omega^2}\,\epsilon^{-ct}+\frac{1}{\omega}\sqrt{\frac{(a-b)^2+\omega^2}{(c-b)^2+\omega^2}}\,\epsilon^{-bt}\sin(\omega t+\phi)$ $\phi=\tan^{-1}\left(\frac{\omega}{a-b}\right)-\tan^{-1}\left(\frac{\omega}{c-b}\right)$
167	$\frac{s+a}{s(s+c)\left[(s+b)^2+\omega^2\right]}$	$\frac{a}{c(b^2+\omega^2)}+\frac{(c-a)}{c\left[(b-c)^2+\omega^2\right]}\,\epsilon^{-ct}-\frac{1}{\omega\sqrt{b^2+\omega^2}}\sqrt{\frac{(a-b)^2+\omega^2}{(b-c)^2+\omega^2}}\,\epsilon^{-bt}\sin(\omega t+\phi)$ $\phi=\tan^{-1}\left(\frac{\omega}{b}\right)+\tan^{-1}\left(\frac{\omega}{a-b}\right)+\tan^{-1}\left(\frac{\omega}{b-c}\right)$
168	$\frac{s+a}{s^2(s+c)\left[(s+b)^2+\omega^2\right]}$	$\frac{a}{c(b^2+\omega^2)}\left[t+\frac{1}{a}-\frac{1}{c}-\frac{2b}{(b^2+\omega^2)}\right]+\frac{(a-c)}{c^2\left[\omega^2+(c-b)^2\right]}\,\epsilon^{-ct}$ $+\frac{1}{\omega(b^2+\omega^2)}\sqrt{\frac{(a-b)^2+\omega^2}{(c-b)^2+\omega^2}}\,\epsilon^{-bt}\sin(\omega t+\phi)$ $\phi=\tan^{-1}\left(\frac{\omega}{a-b}\right)-\tan^{-1}\left(\frac{\omega}{c-b}\right)+2\tan^{-1}\left(\frac{\omega}{b}\right)$
169	$\frac{s+a}{(s+c)(s+d)\left[(s+b)^2+\omega^2\right]}$	$\frac{(d-a)}{(d-c)\left[(b-d)^2+\omega^2\right]}\,\epsilon^{-dt}+\frac{(c-a)}{(c-d)\left[(b-c)^2+\omega^2\right]}\,\epsilon^{-ct}$ $+\frac{1}{\omega}\sqrt{\frac{(a-b)^2+\omega^2}{\left[(b-d)^2+\omega^2\right]\left[(b-c)^2+\omega^2\right]}}\,\epsilon^{-bt}\cos(\omega t+\phi)$ $\phi=\tan^{-1}\left(\frac{\omega}{a-b}\right)-\tan^{-1}\left(\frac{b-d}{\omega}\right)-\tan^{-1}\left(\frac{\omega}{c-b}\right)$

NO.	F(s)	f(t)
170	$\dfrac{s+a}{(s+c)^2\left[(s+b)^2+\omega^2\right]}$	$\left[\dfrac{(a-c)}{(b-c)^2+\omega^2}t+\dfrac{\left[b^2+\omega^2+2a(c-b)-c^2\right]}{\left[(b-c)^2+\omega^2\right]^2}\right]\epsilon^{-ct}+\dfrac{\sqrt{(a-b)^2+\omega^2}}{\omega\left[(b-c)^2+\omega^2\right]}\epsilon^{-bt}\sin(\omega t+\phi)$ $\phi=\tan^{-1}\left(\dfrac{\omega}{a-b}\right)-2\tan^{-1}\left(\dfrac{\omega}{c-b}\right)$
171	$\dfrac{s+a}{s(s+c)^2\left[(s+b)^2+\omega^2\right]}$	$\dfrac{a}{c^2(b^2+\omega^2)}+\dfrac{\epsilon^{-bt}}{\omega\left[(c-b)^2+\omega^2\right]}\sqrt{\dfrac{(b-a)^2+\omega^2}{b^2+\omega^2}}\sin(\omega t+\phi)$ $+\left[\dfrac{2c(a-c)(b-c)-a\left[(c-b)^2+\omega^2\right]}{c^2\left[(c-b)^2+\omega^2\right]^2}+\dfrac{(c-a)}{c\left[(c-b)^2+\omega^2\right]}t\right]\epsilon^{-ct}$ $\phi=\tan^{-1}\left(\dfrac{\omega}{b}\right)-2\tan^{-1}\left(\dfrac{\omega}{c-b}\right)-\tan^{-1}\left(\dfrac{\omega}{b-a}\right)$
172	$\dfrac{s+a}{s^2(s+c)^2\left[(s+b)^2+\omega^2\right]}$	$\dfrac{a}{c^2(b^2+\omega^2)}t+\dfrac{(c-2a)(b^2+\omega^2)-2abc}{c^3(b^2+\omega^2)^2}+\dfrac{\sqrt{(b-a)^2+\omega^2}}{\omega(b^2+\omega^2)\left[(b-c)^2+\omega^2\right]}\epsilon^{-bt}\sin(\omega t+\phi)$ $+\left[\dfrac{(2a-c)\left[(c-b)^2+\omega^2\right]-2c(a-c)(b-c)}{c^3\left[(c-b)^2+\omega^2\right]^2}+\dfrac{(a-c)}{c^2\left[(c-b)^2+\omega^2\right]}t\right]\epsilon^{-ct}$ $\phi=\tan^{-1}\left(\dfrac{\omega}{b}\right)-\tan^{-1}\left(\dfrac{b}{\omega}\right)+\tan^{-1}\left(\dfrac{c-b}{\omega}\right)-\tan^{-1}\left(\dfrac{\omega}{c-b}\right)+\tan^{-1}\left(\dfrac{\omega}{a-b}\right)$
173	$\dfrac{s+a}{(s+d)(s+c)^2\left[(s+b)^2+\omega^2\right]}$	$\dfrac{(a-d)}{(d-c)^2\left[(d-b)^2+\omega^2\right]}\epsilon^{-dt}+\dfrac{\epsilon^{-bt}}{\omega\left[(b-c)^2+\omega^2\right]}\sqrt{\dfrac{(b-a)^2+\omega^2}{(b-d)^2+\omega^2}}\sin(\omega t+\phi)$ $+\left[\dfrac{(d-a)\left[(c-b)^2+\omega^2\right]-2(b-c)(d-c)(a-c)}{(c-d)^2\left[(c-b)^2+\omega^2\right]^2}+\dfrac{(a-c)}{(d-c)\left[(c-b)^2+\omega^2\right]}t\right]\epsilon^{-ct}$ $\phi=\tan^{-1}\left(\dfrac{\omega}{a-b}\right)-2\tan^{-1}\left(\dfrac{\omega}{c-b}\right)-\tan^{-1}\left(\dfrac{\omega}{d-b}\right)$
174	$\dfrac{s+a}{(s^2+c^2)\left[(s+b)^2+\omega^2\right]}$	$\dfrac{1}{c}\sqrt{\dfrac{a^2+c^2}{(b^2+\omega^2-c^2)^2+4c^2b^2}}\sin(ct+\phi_1)+\dfrac{1}{\omega}\sqrt{\dfrac{(a-b)^2+\omega^2}{(b^2-\omega^2+c^2)^2+4\omega^2b^2}}\epsilon^{-bt}\sin(\omega t+\phi_2)$ $\phi_1=\tan^{-1}\left(\dfrac{c}{a}\right)-\tan^{-1}\left(\dfrac{2bc}{b^2+\omega^2-c^2}\right),\ \phi_2=\tan^{-1}\left(\dfrac{\omega}{a-b}\right)-\tan^{-1}\left(\dfrac{-2b\omega}{b^2+c^2-\omega^2}\right)$
175	$\dfrac{s+a}{s(s^2+c^2)\left[(s+b)^2+\omega^2\right]}$	$\dfrac{a}{c^2(b^2+\omega^2)}+\dfrac{1}{c^2}\sqrt{\dfrac{a^2+c^2}{\left[(b^2+\omega^2-c^2)^2+4b^2c^2\right]}}\sin(ct+\phi_1)$ $+\dfrac{1}{\omega}\sqrt{\dfrac{(a-b)^2+\omega^2}{\left[b^2+\omega^2\right]\left[(b^2-\omega^2+c^2)^2+4b^2\omega^2\right]}}\epsilon^{-bt}\sin(\omega t+\phi_2)$ $\phi_1=\tan^{-1}\left(\dfrac{c}{a}\right)-\tan^{-1}\left(\dfrac{2bc}{b^2+\omega^2-c^2}\right)-\dfrac{\pi}{2},\ \phi_2=\tan^{-1}\left(\dfrac{\omega}{a-b}\right)-\tan^{-1}\left(\dfrac{\omega}{-b}\right)-\tan^{-1}\left(\dfrac{-2b\omega}{b^2-\omega^2+c^2}\right)$
176	$\dfrac{s+a}{(s+d)(s^2+c^2)\left[(s+b)^2+\omega^2\right]}$	$\dfrac{(a-d)}{(c^2+d^2)\left[(b-d)^2+\omega^2\right]}\epsilon^{-dt}+\dfrac{1}{c}\sqrt{\dfrac{a^2+c^2}{(d^2+c^2)\left[(b^2+\omega^2-c^2)^2+4b^2c^2\right]}}\sin(ct+\phi_1)$ $+\dfrac{1}{\omega}\sqrt{\dfrac{(a-b)^2+\omega^2}{\left[(d-b)^2+\omega^2\right]\left[(b^2-\omega^2+c^2)^2+4b^2\omega^2\right]}}\epsilon^{-bt}\sin(\omega t+\phi_2)$ $\phi_1=\tan^{-1}\left(\dfrac{c}{a}\right)-\tan^{-1}\left(\dfrac{c}{d}\right)-\tan^{-1}\left(\dfrac{2bc}{b^2+\omega^2-c^2}\right),\ \phi_2=\tan^{-1}\left(\dfrac{\omega}{a-b}\right)-\tan^{-1}\left(\dfrac{\omega}{d-b}\right)-\tan^{-1}\left(\dfrac{-2b\omega}{b^2-\omega^2+c^2}\right)$

NO.	F(s)	f(t)
177	$\frac{s+a}{[(s+a)^2+\omega^2]^2}$	$\frac{1}{2\omega} t\epsilon^{-at} \sin \omega t$
178	$\frac{s+a}{[(s+b)^2+\omega^2]^2}$	$\frac{a-b}{2\omega^3} \epsilon^{-bt} \sin \omega t - \frac{1}{2\omega^2} \sqrt{(a-b)^2+\omega^2}\, t\epsilon^{-bt} \cos(\omega t+\phi)$; $\phi = \tan^{-1}\left(\frac{\omega}{a-b}\right)$
179	$\frac{s+a}{[(s+b)^2+\omega^2][(s+c)^2+d^2]}$	$\frac{1}{\omega}\sqrt{\frac{(a-b)^2+\omega^2}{\{[(c-b)^2+\omega^2]-d^2\}^2+4d^2(c-b)^2}}\, \epsilon^{-bt} \cos(\omega t-\phi_1)$ $+\frac{1}{d}\sqrt{\frac{(a-c)^2+d^2}{\{[(c-b)^2+\omega^2]-d^2\}^2+4d^2(c-b)^2}}\, \epsilon^{-ct} \cos(dt-\phi_2)$ $\phi_1 = \tan^{-1}\left(\frac{a-b}{\omega}\right) + \tan^{-1}\left[\frac{2\omega(c-b)}{(c-b)^2-\omega^2+d^2}\right]$ $\phi_2 = \tan^{-1}\left(\frac{a-c}{d}\right) + \tan^{-1}\left[\frac{2d(b-c)}{(c-b)^2-d^2+\omega^2}\right]$
180	$\frac{s+a}{[(s+a)^2-\omega^2]}$	$\epsilon^{-at} \cosh \omega t$
181	$\frac{s+a}{(s+b)^3}$	$\left[t+\left(\frac{a-b}{2}\right)t^2\right]\epsilon^{-bt}$
182	$\frac{s+a}{s(s+b)^3}$	$\frac{1}{b^3}\left\{a+\left[\frac{b^2(b-a)}{2}t^2-a-abt\right]\epsilon^{-bt}\right\}$
183	$\frac{s+a}{s^2(s+b)^3}$	$\frac{a}{b^3}t+\frac{b-3a}{b^4}+\left[\frac{3a-b}{b^4}+\frac{a-b}{2b^2}t^2+\frac{2a-b}{b^3}t\right]\epsilon^{-bt}$
184	$\frac{s+a}{(s+c)(s+b)^3}$	$\frac{a-c}{(b-c)^3}\epsilon^{-ct}+\left[\frac{a-b}{2(c-b)}t^2+\frac{c-a}{(c-b)^2}t+\frac{a-c}{(c-b)^3}\right]\epsilon^{-bt}$
185	$\frac{s^2}{(s+a)(s+b)(s+c)}$	$\frac{a^2}{(b-a)(c-a)}\epsilon^{-at}+\frac{b^2}{(a-b)(c-b)}\epsilon^{-bt}+\frac{c^2}{(a-c)(b-c)}\epsilon^{-ct}$
186	$\frac{s^2}{(s+a)(s+b)^2}$	$\frac{a^2}{(b-a)^2}\epsilon^{-at}+\left[\frac{b^2}{(a-b)}t+\frac{b^2-2ab}{(a-b)^2}\right]\epsilon^{-bt}$
187	$\frac{s^2}{(s+a)^3}$	$\left[2-2at+\frac{a^2}{2}t^2\right]\epsilon^{-at}$
188	$\frac{s^2}{(s+a)(s^2+\omega^2)}$	$\frac{a^2}{(a^2+\omega^2)}\epsilon^{-at}-\frac{\omega}{\sqrt{a^2+\omega^2}}\sin(\omega t+\phi)$; $\phi=-\tan^{-1}\left(\frac{\omega}{a}\right)$
189	$\frac{s^2}{(s+a)^2(s^2+\omega^2)}$	$\left[\frac{a^2}{(a^2+\omega^2)}t-\frac{2a\omega^2}{(a^2+\omega^2)^2}\right]\epsilon^{-at}-\frac{\omega}{(a^2+\omega^2)}\sin(\omega t+\phi)$ $\phi=-2\tan^{-1}\left(\frac{\omega}{a}\right)$
190	$\frac{s^2}{(s+a)(s+b)(s^2+\omega^2)}$	$\frac{a^2}{(b-a)(a^2+\omega^2)}\epsilon^{-at}+\frac{b^2}{(a-b)(b^2+\omega^2)}\epsilon^{-bt}-\frac{\omega}{\sqrt{(a^2+\omega^2)(b^2+\omega^2)}}\sin(\omega t+\phi)$ $\phi=-\left[\tan^{-1}\left(\frac{\omega}{a}\right)+\tan^{-1}\left(\frac{\omega}{b}\right)\right]$

NO.	F(s)	f(t)
191	$\frac{s^2}{(s+a)(s+b)^2(s^2+\omega^2)}$	$\frac{a^2}{(b-a)^2(a^2+\omega^2)}\epsilon^{-at}-\frac{\omega}{(b^2+\omega^2)\sqrt{(a^2+\omega^2)}}\sin(\omega t+\phi)+\frac{b^2}{(a-b)(b^2+\omega^2)}t\epsilon^{-bt}$ $-\left[\frac{2b(a-b)(b^2+\omega^2)+b^2(3b^2+\omega^2-2ab)}{(a-b)^2(b^2+\omega^2)^2}\right]\epsilon^{-bt}$ $\phi=-\left[\tan^{-1}\left(\frac{\omega}{a}\right)+2\tan^{-1}\left(\frac{\omega}{b}\right)\right]$
192	$\frac{s^2}{(s^2+a^2)(s^2+\omega^2)}$	$-\frac{a}{(\omega^2-a^2)}\sin(at)-\frac{\omega}{(a^2-\omega^2)}\sin(\omega t)$
193	$\frac{s^2}{(s^2+\omega^2)^2}$	$\frac{1}{2\omega}(\sin\omega t+\omega t\cos\omega t)$
194	$\frac{s^2}{(s+a)\left[(s+b)^2+\omega^2\right]}$	$\frac{a^2}{(a-b)^2+\omega^2}\epsilon^{-at}+\frac{1}{\omega}\sqrt{\frac{(b^2-\omega^2)^2+4b^2\omega^2}{(a-b)^2+\omega^2}}\epsilon^{-bt}\sin(\omega t+\phi)$ $\phi=\tan^{-1}\left(\frac{-2b\omega}{b^2-\omega^2}\right)-\tan^{-1}\left(\frac{\omega}{a-b}\right)$
195	$\frac{s^2}{(s+a)^2\left[(s+b)^2+\omega^2\right]}$	$\frac{a^2}{(b-a)^2+\omega^2}t\epsilon^{-at}-2\left[\frac{a\left[(b-a)^2+\omega^2\right]+a^2(b-a)}{\left[(b-a)^2+\omega^2\right]^2}\right]\epsilon^{-at}$ $+\frac{\sqrt{(b^2-\omega^2)^2+4b^2\omega^2}}{\omega\left[(a-b)^2+\omega^2\right]}\epsilon^{-bt}\sin(\omega t+\phi)$ $\phi=\tan^{-1}\left(\frac{-2b\omega}{b^2-\omega^2}\right)-2\tan^{-1}\left(\frac{\omega}{a-b}\right)$
196	$\frac{s^2}{(s+a)(s+b)\left[(s+c)^2+\omega^2\right]}$	$\frac{a^2}{(b-a)\left[(c-a)^2+\omega^2\right]}\epsilon^{-at}+\frac{b^2}{(a-b)\left[(c-b)^2+\omega^2\right]}\epsilon^{-bt}$ $+\frac{1}{\omega}\sqrt{\frac{(c^2-\omega^2)^2+4c^2\omega^2}{\left[(b-c)^2+\omega^2\right]\left[(a-c)^2+\omega^2\right]}}\epsilon^{-ct}\sin(\omega t+\phi)$ $\phi=\tan^{-1}\left(\frac{-2c\omega}{c^2-\omega^2}\right)-\tan^{-1}\left(\frac{\omega}{a-c}\right)-\tan^{-1}\left(\frac{\omega}{b-c}\right)$
197	$\frac{s^2}{(s^2+a^2)\left[(s+b)^2+\omega^2\right]}$	$\frac{-a}{\sqrt{(b^2+\omega^2-a^2)^2+4a^2b^2}}\sin(at+\phi_1)+\frac{1}{\omega}\sqrt{\frac{(b^2-\omega^2)^2+4b^2\omega^2}{(b^2+\omega^2-a^2)^2+4a^2b^2}}\epsilon^{-bt}\sin(\omega t+\phi_2)$ $\phi_1=-\tan^{-1}\left(\frac{2ab}{b^2+\omega^2-a^2}\right),\ \phi_2=\tan^{-1}\left(\frac{-2b\omega}{b^2-\omega^2}\right)-\tan^{-1}\left(\frac{-2b\omega}{b^2+a^2-\omega^2}\right)$
198	$\frac{s^2}{\left[(s+a)^2+\omega^2\right]^2}$	$\frac{a^2+\omega^2}{2\omega^3}\epsilon^{-at}\sin(\omega t)-\frac{\sqrt{(a^2-\omega^2)^2+4a^2\omega^2}}{2\omega^2}t\epsilon^{-at}\cos(\omega t+\phi)$ $\phi=\tan^{-1}\left(\frac{-2a\omega}{a^2-\omega^2}\right)$

NO.	F(s)	f(t)
199	$\frac{s^2}{[(s+a)^2+\omega^2][(s+b)^2+c^2]}$	$\frac{1}{\omega}\sqrt{\frac{(a^2-\omega^2)^2+4a^2\omega^2}{\{[(b-a)^2-\omega^2]+c^2\}^2+4\omega^2(b-a)^2}}\,\epsilon^{-at}\cos(\omega t-\phi_1)$ $+\frac{1}{c}\sqrt{\frac{(b^2-c^2)^2+4b^2c^2}{\{[(b-a)^2+\omega^2]-c^2\}^2+4c^2(b-a)^2}}\,\epsilon^{-bt}\cos(ct-\phi_2)$ $\phi_1=\tan^{-1}\left(\frac{a^2-\omega^2}{2a\omega}\right)+\tan^{-1}\left[\frac{2\omega(b-a)}{(b-a)^2-\omega^2+c^2}\right]$, $\phi_2=\tan^{-1}\left(\frac{b^2-c^2}{2bc}\right)+\tan^{-1}\left[\frac{2c(a-b)}{(b-a)^2+\omega^2-c^2}\right]$
200	$\frac{s^2}{s^3+a^3}$	$\frac{1}{3}\left(\epsilon^{-at}+2\epsilon^{\frac{a}{2}t}\cos\frac{\sqrt{3}}{2}at\right)$
201	$\frac{s^2}{s^4+4\omega^4}$	$\frac{1}{2\omega}(\sin\omega t\cosh\omega t+\cos\omega t\sinh\omega t)$
202	$\frac{s^2}{s^4-\omega^4}$	$\frac{1}{2\omega}(\sinh\omega t+\sin\omega t)$
203	$\frac{s^2+a}{s^2(s+b)}$	$\frac{b^2+a}{b^2}\epsilon^{-bt}+\frac{a}{b}t-\frac{a}{b^2}$
204	$\frac{s^2+a}{s^3(s+b)}$	$\frac{a}{2b}t^2-\frac{a}{b^2}t+\frac{1}{b^3}\left[b^2+a-(a+b^2)\epsilon^{-bt}\right]$
205	$\frac{s^2+a}{s(s+b)(s+c)}$	$\frac{a}{bc}+\frac{(b^2+a)}{b(b-c)}\epsilon^{-bt}-\frac{(c^2+a)}{c(b-c)}\epsilon^{-ct}$
206	$\frac{s^2+a}{s^2(s+b)(s+c)}$	$\frac{b^2+a}{b^2(c-b)}\epsilon^{-bt}+\frac{c^2+a}{c^2(b-c)}\epsilon^{-ct}+\frac{a}{bc}t-\frac{a(b+c)}{b^2c^2}$
207	$\frac{s^2+a}{(s+b)(s+c)(s+d)}$	$\frac{b^2+a}{(c-b)(d-b)}\epsilon^{-bt}+\frac{c^2+a}{(b-c)(d-c)}\epsilon^{-ct}+\frac{d^2+a}{(b-d)(c-d)}\epsilon^{-dt}$
208	$\frac{s^2+a}{s(s+b)(s+c)(s+d)}$	$\frac{a}{bcd}+\frac{b^2+a}{b(b-c)(d-b)}\epsilon^{-bt}+\frac{c^2+a}{c(b-c)(c-d)}\epsilon^{-ct}+\frac{d^2+a}{d(b-d)(d-c)}\epsilon^{-dt}$
209	$\frac{s^2+a}{s^2(s+b)(s+c)(s+d)}$	$\frac{a}{bcd}t-\frac{a}{b^2c^2d^2}(bc+cd+db)+\frac{b^2+a}{b^2(b-c)(b-d)}\epsilon^{-bt}+\frac{c^2+a}{c^2(c-b)(c-d)}\epsilon^{-ct}$ $+\frac{d^2+a}{d^2(d-b)(d-c)}\epsilon^{-dt}$
210	$\frac{s^2+a}{(s+b)(s+c)(s+d)(s+f)}$	$\frac{b^2+a}{(c-b)(d-b)(f-b)}\epsilon^{-bt}+\frac{c^2+a}{(b-c)(d-c)(f-c)}\epsilon^{-ct}+\frac{d^2+a}{(b-d)(c-d)(f-d)}\epsilon^{-dt}$ $+\frac{f^2+a}{(b-f)(c-f)(d-f)}\epsilon^{-ft}$
211	$\frac{s^2+a}{s(s+b)(s+c)(s+d)(s+f)}$	$\frac{a}{bcdf}-\frac{b^2+a}{b(c-b)(d-b)(f-b)}\epsilon^{-bt}-\frac{c^2+a}{c(b-c)(d-c)(f-c)}\epsilon^{-ct}$ $-\frac{d^2+a}{d(b-d)(c-d)(f-d)}\epsilon^{-dt}-\frac{f^2+a}{f(b-f)(c-f)(d-f)}\epsilon^{-ft}$

NO.	F(s)	f(t)
212	$\frac{s^2+a}{(s+b)(s+c)(s+d)(s+f)(s+g)}$	$\frac{b^2+a}{(c-b)(d-b)(f-b)(g-b)}\epsilon^{-bt}+\frac{c^2+a}{(b-c)(d-c)(f-c)(g-c)}\epsilon^{-ct}+\frac{d^2+a}{(b-d)(c-d)(f-d)(g-d)}\epsilon^{-dt}$ $+\frac{f^2+a}{(b-f)(c-f)(d-f)(g-f)}\epsilon^{-ft}+\frac{g^2+a}{(b-g)(c-g)(d-g)(f-g)}\epsilon^{-gt}$
213	$\frac{s^2+a}{(s+b)(s+c)(s+d)^2}$	$\frac{b^2+a}{(c-b)(d-b)^2}\epsilon^{-bt}+\frac{c^2+a}{(b-c)(d-c)^2}\epsilon^{-ct}+\frac{d^2+a}{(b-d)(c-d)}t\epsilon^{-dt}$ $+\frac{a(2d-b-c)+d[d(b+c)-2bc]}{(b-d)^2(c-d)^2}\epsilon^{-dt}$
214	$\frac{s^2+a}{s(s+b)(s+c)(s+d)^2}$	$\frac{a}{bcd^2}-\frac{d^2+a}{d(c-d)(b-d)}t\epsilon^{-dt}+\frac{2}{(c-d)(b-d)}\epsilon^{-dt}-\frac{b^2+a}{b(d-b)^2(c-b)}\epsilon^{-bt}$ $-\frac{[(b-d)(c-d)-d(b-d)-d(c-d)](d^2+a)}{d^2(b-d)^2(c-d)^2}\epsilon^{-dt}-\frac{c^2+a}{c(b-c)(d-c)^2}\epsilon^{-ct}$
215	$\frac{s^2+a}{s(s+b)^2}$	$\frac{a}{b^2}-\frac{(a+b^2)}{b}t\epsilon^{-bt}+\frac{(b^2-a)}{b^2}\epsilon^{-bt}$
216	$\frac{s^2+a}{s^2(s+b)^2}$	$\frac{a}{b^2}t-\frac{2a}{b^3}+\frac{1}{b^2}\left[(b^2+a)t+\frac{2a}{b}\right]\epsilon^{-bt}$
217	$\frac{s^2+a}{(s+b)(s+c)^2}$	$\frac{b^2+a}{(c-b)^2}\epsilon^{-bt}+\left[\frac{c^2+a}{(b-c)}t+\frac{c^2-2bc-a}{(b-c)^2}\right]\epsilon^{-ct}$
218	$\frac{s^2+a}{s(s+b)(s+c)^2}$	$\frac{a}{bc^2}-\frac{(b^2+a)}{b(c-b)^2}\epsilon^{-bt}+\left[\frac{c^2+a}{c(c-b)}t+\frac{bc^2+(2c-b)a}{c^2(c-b)^2}\right]\epsilon^{-ct}$
219	$\frac{s^2+a}{s^2(s+b)(s+c)^2}$	$\frac{a}{bc^2}t-\frac{a(c+2b)}{c^3b^2}+\left[\frac{c^2+a}{c^2(b-c)}t-\frac{2}{c(b-c)}+\frac{(2b-3c)(c^2+a)}{c^3(b-c)^2}\right]\epsilon^{-ct}+\frac{b^2+a}{b^2(c-b)^2}\epsilon^{-bt}$
220	$\frac{s^2+a}{(s+b)^2(s+c)^2}$	$\left[\frac{b^2+a}{(c-b)^2}t-\frac{2(bc+a)}{(c-b)^3}\right]\epsilon^{-bt}+\left[\frac{c^2+a}{(c-b)^2}t+\frac{2(bc+a)}{(c-b)^3}\right]\epsilon^{-ct}$
221	$\frac{s^2+a}{s(s+b)^2(s+c)^2}$	$\frac{a}{b^2c^2}-\left[\frac{b^2+a}{b(c-b)^2}t-\frac{2}{(c-b)^2}+\frac{(b^2+a)(c-3b)}{b^2(c-b)^3}\right]\epsilon^{-bt}$ $-\left[\frac{c^2+a}{c(b-c)^2}t-\frac{2}{(b-c)^2}+\frac{(c^2+a)(b-3c)}{c^2(b-c)^3}\right]\epsilon^{-ct}$
222	$\frac{s^2+a}{s^2(s+b)^2(s+c)^2}$	$\frac{a}{b^2c^2}t-\frac{2a(b+c)}{b^3c^3}+\left[\frac{(b^2+a)}{b^2(c-b)^2}t+\frac{2a(c-b)-2b(a+b^2)}{b^3(c-b)^3}\right]\epsilon^{-bt}$ $+\left[\frac{(c^2+a)}{c^2(c-b)^2}t+\frac{2a(b-c)-2c(a+c^2)}{c^3(b-c)^3}\right]\epsilon^{-ct}$
223	$\frac{s^2+a}{(s+d)(s+b)^2(s+c)^2}$	$\left[\frac{b^2+a}{(c-b)^2(d-b)}t-\frac{2b}{(c-b)^2(d-b)}-\frac{(b^2+a)[(c-b)+2(d-b)]}{(c-b)^3(d-b)^2}\right]\epsilon^{-bt}$ $+\left[\frac{c^2+a}{(b-c)^2(d-c)}t-\frac{2c}{(b-c)^2(d-c)}-\frac{(c^2+a)[(b-c)+2(d-c)]}{(b-c)^3(d-c)^2}\right]\epsilon^{-ct}$ $+\frac{d^2+a}{(b-d)^2(c-d)^2}\epsilon^{-dt}$

NO.	F(s)	f(t)
224	$\frac{s^2+a}{s^2(s+b)^3}$	$\left[\frac{b^2+a}{2b^2}t^2+\frac{2a}{b^3}t+\frac{3a}{b^4}\right]\epsilon^{-bt}+\frac{a}{b^3}t-\frac{3a}{b^4}$
225	$\frac{s^2+a}{s(s^2+\omega^2)}$	$\frac{a}{\omega^2}-\frac{(a-\omega^2)}{\omega^2}\cos\omega t$
226	$\frac{s^2+2a^2}{s(s^2+4a^2)}$	$\cos^2 at$
227	$\frac{s^2+a}{s^2(s^2+\omega^2)}$	$\frac{a}{\omega^2}t-\frac{(a-\omega^2)}{\omega^3}\sin\omega t$
228	$\frac{s^2+a}{(s+b)(s^2+\omega^2)}$	$\frac{b^2+a}{b^2+\omega^2}\epsilon^{-bt}+\frac{1}{\omega}\frac{(a-\omega^2)}{\sqrt{(b^2+\omega^2)}}\sin(\omega t+\phi);\ \phi=-\tan^{-1}\left(\frac{\omega}{b}\right)$
229	$\frac{s^2+a}{s(s+b)(s^2+\omega^2)}$	$\frac{a}{b\omega^2}-\frac{b^2+a}{b(b^2+\omega^2)}\epsilon^{-bt}-\frac{1}{\omega^2}\frac{(a-\omega^2)}{\sqrt{(b^2+\omega^2)}}\cos(\omega t+\phi);\ \phi=-\tan^{-1}\left(\frac{\omega}{b}\right)$
230	$\frac{s^2+a}{s^2(s+b)(s^2+\omega^2)}$	$\frac{a}{b\omega^2}t-\frac{a}{b^2\omega^2}+\frac{b^2+a}{b^2(b^2+\omega^2)}\epsilon^{-bt}-\frac{1}{\omega^3}\frac{(a-\omega^2)}{\sqrt{(b^2+\omega^2)}}\sin(\omega t-\phi);\ \phi=\tan^{-1}\left(\frac{\omega}{b}\right)$
231	$\frac{s^2+a}{(s+b)(s+c)(s^2+\omega^2)}$	$\frac{b^2+a}{(c-b)(b^2+\omega^2)}\epsilon^{-bt}+\frac{c^2+a}{(b-c)(c^2+\omega^2)}\epsilon^{-ct}+\frac{1}{\omega}\frac{(a-\omega^2)}{\sqrt{(b^2+\omega^2)(c^2+\omega^2)}}\sin(\omega t+\phi)$ $\phi=-\tan^{-1}\left(\frac{\omega}{b}\right)-\tan^{-1}\left(\frac{\omega}{c}\right)$
232	$\frac{s^2+a}{s(s+b)(s+c)(s^2+\omega^2)}$	$\frac{a}{bc\omega^2}-\frac{(b^2+a)}{b(c-b)(b^2+\omega^2)}\epsilon^{-bt}-\frac{(c^2+a)}{c(b-c)(c^2+\omega^2)}\epsilon^{-ct}-\frac{1}{\omega^2}\frac{(a-\omega^2)}{\sqrt{(b^2+\omega^2)(c^2+\omega^2)}}\cos(\omega t+\phi)$ $\phi=-\tan^{-1}\left(\frac{\omega}{c}\right)-\tan^{-1}\left(\frac{\omega}{b}\right)$
233	$\frac{s^2+a}{s^2(s+b)(s+c)(s^2+\omega^2)}$	$\frac{a}{bc\omega^2}t-\frac{a}{b^2c\omega^2}-\frac{a}{bc^2\omega^2}+\frac{(b^2+a)}{b^2(c-b)(b^2+\omega^2)}\epsilon^{-bt}+\frac{(c^2+a)}{c^2(b-c)(c^2+\omega^2)}\epsilon^{-ct}$ $+\frac{1}{\omega^3}\frac{(a-\omega^2)}{\sqrt{\omega^2(b+c)^2+(\omega^2-bc)^2}}\cos(\omega t+\phi)$ $\phi=\tan^{-1}\left(\frac{c}{\omega}\right)-\tan^{-1}\left(\frac{\omega}{b}\right)$
234	$\frac{s^2+a}{(s+b)(s+c)(s+d)(s^2+\omega^2)}$	$\frac{b^2+a}{(c-b)(d-b)(b^2+\omega^2)}\epsilon^{-bt}+\frac{c^2+a}{(b-c)(d-c)(c^2-\omega^2)}\epsilon^{-ct}+\frac{d^2+a}{(b-d)(c-d)(d^2+\omega^2)}\epsilon^{-dt}$ $+\frac{1}{\omega}\frac{(a-\omega^2)}{\sqrt{(b^2+\omega^2)(c^2+\omega^2)(d^2+\omega^2)}}\sin(\omega t-\phi)$ $\phi=\tan^{-1}\left(\frac{\omega}{b}\right)+\tan^{-1}\left(\frac{\omega}{c}\right)+\tan^{-1}\left(\frac{\omega}{d}\right)$
235	$\frac{s^2+a}{(s+b)^2(s^2+\omega^2)}$	$\frac{(a-\omega^2)}{\omega(b^2+\omega^2)}\sin(\omega t+\phi)+\left[\frac{b^2+a}{b^2+\omega^2}t+\frac{2b(a-\omega^2)}{(b^2+\omega^2)^2}\right]\epsilon^{-bt}$ $\phi=-2\tan^{-1}\left(\frac{\omega}{b}\right)$

NO.	F(s)	f(t)
236	$\frac{s^2+a}{s(s+b)^2(s^2+\omega^2)}$	$\frac{a}{b^2\omega^2} - \frac{(a-\omega^2)}{\omega^2(b^2+\omega^2)}\cos(\omega t+\phi) - \frac{(b^2+a)}{b(b^2+\omega^2)} t\epsilon^{-bt} + \frac{[2b^2(b^2+\omega^2)-(b^2+a)(3b^2+\omega^2)]}{b^2(b^2+\omega^2)^2}\epsilon^{-bt}$; $\phi = -2\tan^{-1}\left(\frac{\omega}{b}\right)$
237	$\frac{s^2+a}{(s+c)(s+b)^2(s^2+\omega^2)}$	$\frac{c^2+a}{(c^2+\omega^2)(b-c)^2}\epsilon^{-ct} + \frac{1}{\omega(b^2+\omega^2)}\sqrt{\frac{(a-\omega^2)}{(c^2+\omega^2)}}\sin(\omega t+\phi) + \frac{b^2+a}{(c-b)(b^2+\omega^2)} t\epsilon^{-bt} - \frac{[2b(c-b)(b^2+\omega^2)+(b^2+a)(3b^2+\omega^2-2bc)]}{(c-b)^2(b^2+\omega^2)^2}\epsilon^{-bt}$ $\phi = -\tan^{-1}\left(\frac{\omega}{c}\right) - 2\tan^{-1}\left(\frac{\omega}{b}\right)$
238	$\frac{s^2+a}{(s^2+b^2)(s^2+\omega^2)}$	$\frac{(a-b^2)}{b(\omega^2-b^2)}\sin bt + \frac{(a-\omega^2)}{\omega(b^2-\omega^2)}\sin\omega t$
239	$\frac{s^2+a}{s(s^2+b^2)(s^2+\omega^2)}$	$\frac{a}{b^2\omega^2} - \frac{(a-b^2)}{b^2(\omega^2-b^2)}\cos bt - \frac{(a-\omega^2)}{\omega^2(b^2-\omega^2)}\cos\omega t$
240	$\frac{s^2+a}{(s+c)(s^2+b^2)(s^2+\omega^2)}$	$\frac{c^2+a}{(c^2+b^2)(c^2+\omega^2)}\epsilon^{-ct} + \frac{1}{b(\omega^2-b^2)}\sqrt{\frac{(a-b^2)}{c^2+b^2}}\sin(bt-\phi_1) + \frac{1}{\omega(b^2-\omega^2)}\sqrt{\frac{(a-\omega^2)}{c^2+\omega^2}}\sin(\omega t-\phi_2)$ $\phi_1 = \tan^{-1}\left(\frac{b}{c}\right)$; $\phi_2 = \tan^{-1}\left(\frac{\omega}{c}\right)$
241	$\frac{s^2+a}{(s^2+\omega^2)^2}$	$\frac{1}{2\omega^3}\cdot(a+\omega^2)\sin\omega t - \frac{1}{2\omega^2}\cdot(a-\omega^2)\, t\cos\omega t$
242	$\frac{s^2-\omega^2}{(s^2+\omega^2)^2}$	$t\cos\omega t$
243	$\frac{s^2+a}{s(s^2+\omega^2)^2}$	$\frac{a}{\omega^4} - \frac{(a-\omega^2)}{2\omega^3} t\sin\omega t - \frac{a}{\omega^4}\cos\omega t$
244	$\frac{s^2+a}{s^2(s^2+\omega^2)^2}$	$\frac{a}{\omega^4}t + \frac{(a-\omega^2)}{2\omega^4} t\cos\omega t - \frac{(3a-\omega^2)}{2\omega^5}\sin\omega t$
245	$\frac{s^2+a}{(s+b)(s^2+\omega^2)^2}$	$\frac{b^2+a}{(b^2+\omega^2)^2}\epsilon^{-bt} - \frac{1}{2\omega^2}\sqrt{\frac{(a-\omega^2)}{b^2+\omega^2}}\, t\cos(\omega t+\phi_1) + \frac{1}{2\omega^3(b^2+\omega^2)}\sqrt{[2\omega(a-\omega^2)+2\omega^3]^2+[b(a-\omega^2)+2b\omega^2]^2}\cos(\omega t+\phi_2)$ $\phi_1 = -\tan^{-1}\left(\frac{\omega}{b}\right)$; $\phi_2 = -\tan^{-1}\left[\frac{b(a-\omega^2)+2b\omega^2}{2\omega(a-\omega^2)+2\omega^3}\right] - 2\tan^{-1}\left(\frac{\omega}{b}\right)$
246	$\frac{s^2+a}{s[(s+b)^2+\omega^2]}$	$\frac{a}{b^2+\omega^2} + \frac{1}{\omega}\sqrt{\frac{(b^2-\omega^2+a)^2+4\omega^2b^2}{(b^2+\omega^2)}}\epsilon^{-bt}\sin(\omega t+\phi)$ $\phi = \tan^{-1}\left(\frac{-2b\omega}{b^2-\omega^2+a}\right) - \tan^{-1}\left(\frac{\omega}{-b}\right)$

NO.	F(s)	f(t)
247	$\frac{s^2+a}{s^2\left[(s+b)^2+\omega^2\right]}$	$\frac{a}{b^2\omega^2}t-\frac{2ab}{(b^2+\omega^2)^2}+\frac{1}{\omega(b^2+\omega^2)}\sqrt{(b^2-\omega^2+a)^2+4\omega^2b^2}\ \epsilon^{-bt}\cos(\omega t+\phi)$ $\phi=\tan^{-1}\left(\frac{-2\omega b}{b^2-\omega^2+a}\right)-\tan^{-1}\left(\frac{b}{\omega}\right)+\tan^{-1}\left(\frac{\omega}{b}\right)$
248	$\frac{s^2+a}{(s+c)\left[(s+b)^2+\omega^2\right]}$	$\frac{c^2+a}{(b-c)^2+\omega^2}\epsilon^{-ct}+\frac{1}{\omega}\sqrt{\frac{(b^2-\omega^2+a)^2+4b^2\omega^2}{(b-c)^2+\omega^2}}\ \epsilon^{-bt}\sin(\omega t+\phi)$ $\phi=\tan^{-1}\left(\frac{-2b\omega}{b^2-\omega^2+a}\right)-\tan^{-1}\frac{\omega}{c-b}$
249	$\frac{s^2+a}{s(s+c)\left[(s+b)^2+\omega^2\right]}$	$\frac{a}{c(b^2+\omega^2)}-\frac{c^2+a}{c\left[(b-c)^2+\omega^2\right]}\epsilon^{-ct}-\frac{1}{\omega}\sqrt{\frac{(b^2-\omega^2+a)^2+4b^2\omega^2}{(b^2+\omega^2)\left[(b-c)^2+\omega^2\right]}}\ \epsilon^{-bt}\cos(\omega t+\phi)$ $\phi=\tan^{-1}\left(\frac{-2b\omega}{b^2-\omega^2+a}\right)-\tan^{-1}\left(\frac{b}{\omega}\right)-\tan^{-1}\left(\frac{\omega}{c-b}\right)$
250	$\frac{s^2+a}{s^2(s+c)\left[(s+b)^2+\omega^2\right]}$	$\frac{a}{c(b^2+\omega^2)}t-\frac{a(b^2+\omega^2+2bc)}{c^2(b^2+\omega^2)^2}+\frac{c^2+a}{c^2\left[(b-c)^2+\omega^2\right]}\epsilon^{-ct}$ $+\frac{1}{\omega(b^2+\omega^2)}\sqrt{\frac{(b^2-\omega^2+a)^2+4b^2\omega^2}{(b-c)^2+\omega^2}}\ \epsilon^{-bt}\cos(\omega t-\phi)$ $\phi=\tan^{-1}\left(\frac{b^2-\omega^2+a}{-2b\omega}\right)+\tan^{-1}\left(\frac{\omega}{c-b}\right)-2\tan^{-1}\left(\frac{\omega}{b}\right)$
251	$\frac{s^2+a}{(s+c)(s+d)\left[(s+b)^2+\omega^2\right]}$	$\frac{c^2+a}{(d-c)\left[(b-c)^2+\omega^2\right]}\epsilon^{-ct}+\frac{d^2+a}{(c-d)\left[(b-d)^2+\omega^2\right]}\epsilon^{-dt}$ $+\frac{1}{\omega}\sqrt{\frac{(b^2-\omega^2+a)^2+4b^2\omega^2}{\left[(d-b)^2+\omega^2\right]\left[(c-b)^2+\omega^2\right]}}\ \epsilon^{-bt}\sin(\omega t+\phi)$ $\phi=\tan^{-1}\left(\frac{-2b\omega}{b^2-\omega^2+a}\right)-\tan^{-1}\left(\frac{\omega}{c-b}\right)-\tan^{-1}\left(\frac{\omega}{d-b}\right)$
252	$\frac{s^2+a}{s(s+c)(s+d)\left[(s+b)^2+\omega^2\right]}$	$\frac{a}{cd(b^2+\omega^2)}+\frac{c^2+a}{c(c-d)\left[(b-c)^2+\omega^2\right]}\epsilon^{-ct}+\frac{d^2+a}{d(d-c)\left[(b-d)^2+\omega^2\right]}\epsilon^{-dt}$ $-\frac{1}{\omega}\sqrt{\frac{(b^2-\omega^2+a)^2+4b^2\omega^2}{\left[b^2+\omega^2\right]\left[(c-b)^2+\omega^2\right]\left[(d-b)^2+\omega^2\right]}}\ \epsilon^{-bt}\cos(\omega t+\phi)$ $\phi=\tan^{-1}\left(\frac{-2b\omega}{b^2-\omega^2+a}\right)-\tan^{-1}\left(\frac{b}{\omega}\right)-\tan^{-1}\left(\frac{\omega}{c-b}\right)-\tan^{-1}\left(\frac{\omega}{d-b}\right)$
253	$\frac{s^2+a}{(s+c)^2\left[(s+b)^2+\omega^2\right]}$	$\frac{c^2+a}{(b-c)^2+\omega^2}t\epsilon^{-ct}-\frac{2c\left[(b-c)^2+\omega^2\right]+2(b-c)(c^2+a)}{\left[(b-c)^2+\omega^2\right]^2}\epsilon^{-ct}$ $+\frac{\sqrt{(b^2-\omega^2+a)^2+4b^2\omega^2}}{\omega\left[(c-b)^2+\omega^2\right]}\epsilon^{-bt}\sin(\omega t+\phi)$ $\phi=\tan^{-1}\left(\frac{-2b\omega}{b^2-\omega^2+a}\right)-2\tan^{-1}\left(\frac{\omega}{c-b}\right)$

NO.	F(s)	f(t)
254	$\dfrac{s^2+a}{s(s+c)^2\left[(s+b)^2+\omega^2\right]}$	$\dfrac{a}{c^2\left[b^2+\omega^2\right]}-\dfrac{1}{\omega\left[(c-b)^2+\omega^2\right]}\sqrt{\dfrac{(b^2-\omega^2+a)^2+4b^2\omega^2}{\left[b^2+\omega^2\right]}}\,\epsilon^{-bt}\cos(\omega t+\phi)$ $-\left[\dfrac{c^2+a}{c\left[(b-c)^2+\omega^2\right]}t-\dfrac{2}{\left[(b-c)^2+\omega^2\right]}+\dfrac{(c^2+a)\left[(b-c)^2+\omega^2-2c(b-c)\right]}{c^2\left[(b-c)^2+\omega^2\right]^2}\right]\epsilon^{-ct}$ $\phi=\tan^{-1}\left(\dfrac{-2b\omega}{b^2-\omega^2+a}\right)-\tan^{-1}\left(\dfrac{b}{\omega}\right)-2\tan^{-1}\left(\dfrac{\omega}{c-b}\right)$
255	$\dfrac{s^2+a}{(s+c)(s+d)^2\left[(s+b)^2+\omega^2\right]}$	$\dfrac{c^2+a}{(d-c)^2\left[(b-c)^2+\omega^2\right]}\epsilon^{-ct}+\dfrac{1}{\omega\left[(d-b)^2+\omega^2\right]}\sqrt{\dfrac{(b^2-\omega^2+a)^2+4b^2\omega^2}{\left[(c-b)^2+\omega^2\right]}}\,\epsilon^{-bt}\cos(\omega t-\phi)$ $+\left[\dfrac{d^2+a}{(c-d)\left[(b-d)^2+\omega^2\right]}t-\dfrac{2d}{(c-d)\left[(b-d)^2+\omega^2\right]}\right.$ $\left.-\dfrac{(d^2+a)\left[(b-d)^2+\omega^2+2(c-d)(b-d)\right]}{(c-d)^2\left[(b-d)^2+\omega^2\right]^2}\right]\epsilon^{-dt}$ $\phi=\tan^{-1}\left(\dfrac{b^2-\omega^2+a}{-2b\omega}\right)+\tan^{-1}\left(\dfrac{\omega}{c-b}\right)+2\tan^{-1}\left(\dfrac{\omega}{d-b}\right)$
256	$\dfrac{s^2+a}{(s+c)(s+d)(s+f)\left[(s+b)^2+\omega^2\right]}$	$\dfrac{c^2+a}{(d-c)(f-c)\left[(b-c)^2+\omega^2\right]}\epsilon^{-ct}+\dfrac{d^2+a}{(c-d)(f-d)\left[(b-d)^2+\omega^2\right]}\epsilon^{-dt}+\dfrac{f^2+a}{(c-f)(d-f)\left[(b-f)^2+\omega^2\right]}\epsilon^{-ft}$ $+\dfrac{1}{\omega}\sqrt{\dfrac{(b^2-\omega^2+a)^2+4b^2\omega^2}{\left[(c-b)^2+\omega^2\right]\left[(d-b)^2+\omega^2\right]\left[(f-b)^2+\omega^2\right]}}\,\epsilon^{-bt}\cos(\omega t-\phi)$ $\phi=\tan^{-1}\left(\dfrac{b^2-\omega^2+a}{-2b\omega}\right)+\tan^{-1}\left(\dfrac{\omega}{c-b}\right)+\tan^{-1}\left(\dfrac{\omega}{d-b}\right)+\tan^{-1}\left(\dfrac{\omega}{f-b}\right)$
257	$\dfrac{s^2+a}{(s^2+c^2)\left[(s+b)^2+\omega^2\right]}$	$\dfrac{1}{c}\dfrac{a-c^2}{\sqrt{(b^2+\omega^2-c^2)^2+4c^2b^2}}\sin(ct+\phi_1)+\dfrac{1}{\omega}\sqrt{\dfrac{(b^2-\omega^2+a)^2+4b^2\omega^2}{(b^2+\omega^2-c^2)^2+4c^2b^2}}\,\epsilon^{-bt}\sin(\omega t+\phi_2)$ $\phi_1=-\tan^{-1}\left(\dfrac{2cb}{b^2+\omega^2-c^2}\right);\ \phi_2=\tan^{-1}\left(\dfrac{-2b\omega}{b^2-\omega^2+a}\right)-\tan^{-1}\left(\dfrac{-2b\omega}{c^2+b^2-\omega^2}\right)$
258	$\dfrac{s^2+a}{s(s^2+c^2)\left[(s+b)^2+\omega^2\right]}$	$\dfrac{a}{c^2\left[b^2+\omega^2\right]}-\dfrac{1}{c^2}\dfrac{a-c^2}{\sqrt{(b^2+\omega^2-c^2)^2+4b^2c^2}}\cos(ct+\phi_1)$ $-\dfrac{1}{\omega}\sqrt{\dfrac{(b^2-\omega^2+a)^2+4b^2\omega^2}{(b^2+\omega^2)\left[(b^2+\omega^2-c^2)^2+4b^2c^2\right]}}\,\epsilon^{-bt}\cos(\omega t+\phi_2)$ $\phi_1=-\tan^{-1}\left(\dfrac{2bc}{b^2+\omega^2-c^2}\right);\ \phi_2=\tan^{-1}\left(\dfrac{-2b\omega}{b^2-\omega^2+a}\right)-\tan^{-1}\left(\dfrac{b^2-\omega^2+c^2}{2b\omega}\right)+\tan^{-1}\left(\dfrac{\omega}{b}\right)$
259	$\dfrac{s^2+a}{(s+d)(s^2+c^2)\left[(s+b)^2+\omega^2\right]}$	$\dfrac{d^2+a}{(d^2+c^2)\left[(b-d)^2+\omega^2\right]}\epsilon^{-dt}+\dfrac{1}{c}\dfrac{a-c^2}{\sqrt{(d^2+c^2)\left[(b^2+\omega^2-c^2)^2+4b^2c^2\right]}}\sin(ct-\phi_1)$ $+\dfrac{1}{\omega}\sqrt{\dfrac{(b^2-\omega^2+a)^2+4b^2\omega^2}{\left[(d-b)^2+\omega^2\right]\left[(b^2+\omega^2-c^2)^2+4b^2c^2\right]}}\,\epsilon^{-bt}\cos(\omega t-\phi_2)$ $\phi_1=\tan^{-1}\left(\dfrac{c}{d}\right)+\tan^{-1}\left(\dfrac{2bc}{b^2+\omega^2-c^2}\right)$ $\phi_2=\tan^{-1}\left(\dfrac{b^2-\omega^2+a}{-2b\omega}\right)+\tan^{-1}\left(\dfrac{\omega}{d-b}\right)-\tan^{-1}\left(\dfrac{2b\omega}{b^2-\omega^2+c^2}\right)$

NO.	F(s)	f(t)
260	$\dfrac{s^2+a}{\left[(s+b)^2+\omega^2\right]^2}$	$\dfrac{b^2+\omega^2+a}{2\omega^3}\,\epsilon^{-bt}\sin\omega t-\dfrac{\sqrt{(b^2-\omega^2+a)^2+4b^2\omega^2}}{2\omega^2}\,t\epsilon^{-bt}\cos(\omega t+\phi)$ $\phi=\tan^{-1}\left(\dfrac{-2b\omega}{b^2-\omega^2+a}\right)$
261	$\dfrac{s^2+a}{s\left[(s+b)^2+\omega^2\right]^2}$	$\dfrac{a}{(b^2+\omega^2)^2}-\dfrac{1}{2\omega^2}\sqrt{\dfrac{(b^2-\omega^2+a)^2+4b^2\omega^2}{b^2+\omega^2}}\,t\epsilon^{-bt}\cos(\omega t+\phi_1)$ $+\dfrac{\sqrt{\left[2\omega(b^2+a)\right]^2+\left[ab+b^3-b\omega^2\right]^2}}{2\omega^3\left[b^2+\omega^2\right]}\,\epsilon^{-bt}\cos(\omega t+\phi_2)$ $\phi_1=\tan^{-1}\left(\dfrac{-2b\omega}{b^2-\omega^2+a}\right)-\tan^{-1}\left(\dfrac{\omega}{-b}\right)$ $\phi_2=\tan^{-1}\left(\dfrac{ab+b^3-b\omega^2}{2\omega(b^2+a)}\right)-2\tan^{-1}\left(\dfrac{\omega}{-b}\right)$
262	$\dfrac{s^2+a}{(s+c)\left[(s+b)^2+\omega^2\right]^2}$	$\dfrac{c^2+a}{\left[(b-c)^2+\omega^2\right]^2}\epsilon^{-ct}-\dfrac{1}{2\omega^2}\sqrt{\dfrac{(b^2-\omega^2+a)^2+4b^2\omega^2}{(c-b)^2+\omega^2}}\,t\epsilon^{-bt}\cos(\omega t+\phi_1)$ $+\dfrac{\sqrt{\left[2\omega(b^2+a)\right]^2+\left[ab+b^3-ca-cb^2-\omega^2(b+c)\right]^2}}{2\omega^3\left[(c-b)^2+\omega^2\right]}\,\epsilon^{-bt}\cos(\omega t+\phi_2)$ $\phi_1=\tan^{-1}\left(\dfrac{-2b\omega}{b^2-\omega^2+a}\right)-\tan^{-1}\left(\dfrac{\omega}{c-b}\right)$ $\phi_2=\tan^{-1}\left(\dfrac{ab+b^3-ca-cb^2-\omega^2(b+c)}{2\omega(b^2+a)}\right)-2\tan^{-1}\left(\dfrac{\omega}{c-b}\right)$
263	$\dfrac{s^2+a}{\left[(s+b)^2+\omega^2\right]\left[(s+c)^2+d^2\right]}$	$\dfrac{1}{\omega}\sqrt{\dfrac{(b^2-\omega^2+a)^2+4b^2\omega^2}{\left[(c-b)^2+\omega^2-d^2\right]^2+4d^2(c-b)^2}}\,\epsilon^{-bt}\cos(\omega t-\phi_1)$ $+\dfrac{1}{d}\sqrt{\dfrac{(c^2-d^2+a)^2+4c^2d^2}{\left[(c-b)^2+\omega^2-d^2\right]^2+4d^2(c-b)^2}}\,\epsilon^{-ct}\cos(dt-\phi_2)$ $\phi_1=\tan^{-1}\left(\dfrac{b^2-\omega^2+a}{-2b\omega}\right)+\tan^{-1}\left[\dfrac{2\omega(c-b)}{(c-b)^2-\omega^2+d^2}\right]$ $\phi_2=\tan^{-1}\left(\dfrac{c^2-d^2+a}{-2cd}\right)+\tan^{-1}\left[\dfrac{2d(b-c)}{(c-b)^2-d^2+\omega^2}\right]$
264	$\dfrac{s^2+a}{s\left[(s+b)^2+\omega^2\right]\left[(s+c)^2+d^2\right]}$	$\dfrac{a}{\left[b^2+\omega^2\right]\left[c^2+d^2\right]}-\dfrac{1}{\omega}\sqrt{\dfrac{(b^2-\omega^2+a)^2+4b^2\omega^2}{(b^2+\omega^2)\left\{\left[(c-b)^2+\omega^2-d^2\right]^2+4d^2(c-b)^2\right\}}}\,\epsilon^{-bt}\cos(\omega t+\phi_1)$ $-\dfrac{1}{d}\sqrt{\dfrac{(c^2-d^2+a)^2+4c^2d^2}{(c^2+d^2)\left\{\left[(c-b)^2+\omega^2-d^2\right]^2+4d^2(c-b)^2\right\}}}\,\epsilon^{-ct}\cos(dt+\phi_2)$ $\phi_1=\tan^{-1}\left(\dfrac{-2b\omega}{b^2-\omega^2+a}\right)-\tan^{-1}\left(\dfrac{b}{\omega}\right)-\tan^{-1}\left[\dfrac{2\omega(c-b)}{(c-b)^2-\omega^2+d^2}\right]$ $\phi_2=\tan^{-1}\left(\dfrac{-2cd}{c^2-d^2+a}\right)-\tan^{-1}\left(\dfrac{c}{d}\right)-\tan^{-1}\left[\dfrac{2d(b-c)}{(c-b)^2+\omega^2-d^2}\right]$

NO.	F(s)	f(t)
265	$\dfrac{s^2+a}{(s+f)\left[(s+b)^2+\omega^2\right]\left[(s+c)^2+d^2\right]}$	$\dfrac{f^2+a}{\left[(b-f)^2+\omega^2\right]\left[(c-f)^2+d^2\right]}\epsilon^{-ft}+\dfrac{1}{\omega}\sqrt{\dfrac{(b^2-\omega^2+a)^2+4b^2\omega^2}{\left[(f-b)^2+\omega^2\right]\left\{\left[(c-b)^2+\omega^2-d^2\right]^2+4(c-b)^2d^2\right\}}}\epsilon^{-bt}\cos(\omega t-\phi_1)$ $+\dfrac{1}{d}\sqrt{\dfrac{(c^2-d^2+a)^2+4c^2d^2}{\left[(f-c)^2+d^2\right]\left\{\left[(c-b)^2+\omega^2-d^2\right]^2+4(c-b)^2d^2\right\}}}\epsilon^{-ct}\cos(dt-\phi_2)$ $\phi_1=\tan^{-1}\left(\dfrac{b^2-\omega^2+a}{-2b\omega}\right)+\tan^{-1}\left(\dfrac{\omega}{f-b}\right)+\tan^{-1}\left[\dfrac{2\omega(c-b)}{(c-b)^2-\omega^2+d^2}\right]$ $\phi_2=\tan^{-1}\left(\dfrac{c^2-d^2+a}{-2cd}\right)+\tan^{-1}\left(\dfrac{d}{f-c}\right)+\tan^{-1}\left[\dfrac{2d(b-c)}{(c-b)^2+\omega^2-d^2}\right]$
266	$\dfrac{s(s+a)}{(s+b)(s+c)(s+d)}$	$\dfrac{b^2-ab}{(c-b)(d-b)}\epsilon^{-bt}+\dfrac{c^2-ac}{(b-c)(d-c)}\epsilon^{-ct}+\dfrac{d^2-ad}{(b-d)(c-d)}\epsilon^{-dt}$
267	$\dfrac{s(s+a)}{(s+b)(s+c)(s+d)(s+f)}$	$\dfrac{b^2-ab}{(c-b)(d-b)(f-b)}\epsilon^{-bt}+\dfrac{c^2-ac}{(b-c)(d-c)(f-c)}\epsilon^{-ct}+\dfrac{d^2-ad}{(b-d)(c-d)(f-d)}\epsilon^{-dt}+\dfrac{f^2-af}{(b-f)(c-f)(d-f)}\epsilon^{-ft}$
268	$\dfrac{s(s+a)}{(s+b)(s+c)(s+d)(s+f)(s+g)}$	$\dfrac{b^2-ab}{(c-b)(d-b)(f-b)(g-b)}\epsilon^{-bt}+\dfrac{c^2-ac}{(b-c)(d-c)(f-c)(g-c)}\epsilon^{-ct}+\dfrac{d^2-ad}{(b-d)(c-d)(f-d)(g-d)}\epsilon^{-dt}$ $+\dfrac{f^2-af}{(b-f)(c-f)(d-f)(g-f)}\epsilon^{-ft}+\dfrac{g^2-ag}{(b-g)(c-g)(d-g)(f-g)}\epsilon^{-gt}$
269	$\dfrac{s(s+a)}{(s+b)(s+c)^2}$	$\dfrac{b^2-ab}{(c-b)^2}\epsilon^{-bt}+\left[\dfrac{c^2-ac}{b-c}t+\dfrac{c^2-2bc+ab}{(b-c)^2}\right]\epsilon^{-ct}$
270	$\dfrac{s(s+a)}{(s+b)(s+c)(s+d)^2}$	$\dfrac{b^2-ab}{(c-b)(d-b)^2}\epsilon^{-bt}+\dfrac{c^2-ac}{(b-c)(d-c)^2}\epsilon^{-ct}+\dfrac{d^2-ad}{(b-d)(c-d)}t\epsilon^{-dt}$ $+\dfrac{a(bc-d^2)+d(db+dc-2bc)}{(b-d)^2(c-d)^2}\epsilon^{-dt}$
271	$\dfrac{s(s+a)}{(s+b)(s+c)(s+d)(s+f)^2}$	$\dfrac{b^2-ab}{(c-b)(d-b)(f-b)^2}\epsilon^{-bt}+\dfrac{c^2-ac}{(b-c)(d-c)(f-c)^2}\epsilon^{-ct}+\dfrac{d^2-ad}{(b-d)(c-d)(f-d)^2}\epsilon^{-dt}$ $+\dfrac{f^2-af}{(b-f)(c-f)(d-f)}t\epsilon^{-ft}+\left[\dfrac{a-2f}{(b-f)(c-f)(d-f)}\right.$ $\left.-\dfrac{(f^2-af)\left[(b-f)(c-f)+(b-f)(d-f)+(c-f)(d-f)\right]}{(b-f)^2(c-f)^2(d-f)^2}\right]\epsilon^{-ft}$
272	$\dfrac{s(s+a)}{(s+b)^2(s+c)^2}$	$\left[\dfrac{b^2-ab}{(c-b)^2}t+\dfrac{a(b+c)-2bc}{(c-b)^3}\right]\epsilon^{-bt}+\left[\dfrac{c^2-ac}{(b-c)^2}t+\dfrac{a(b+c)-2bc}{(b-c)^3}\right]\epsilon^{-ct}$
273	$\dfrac{s(s+a)}{(s+d)(s+b)^2(s+c)^2}$	$\dfrac{d^2-ad}{(b-d)^2(c-d)^2}\epsilon^{-dt}+\left[\dfrac{b^2-ab}{(c-b)^2(d-b)}t+\dfrac{a-2b}{(c-b)^2(d-b)}-\dfrac{(b^2-ab)\left[c+2d-3b\right]}{(c-b)^3(d-b)^2}\right]\epsilon^{-bt}$ $+\left[\dfrac{c^2-ac}{(d-c)(b-c)^2}t+\dfrac{a-2c}{(d-c)(b-c)^2}-\dfrac{(c^2-ac)\left[b+2d-3c\right]}{(b-c)^3(d-c)^2}\right]\epsilon^{-ct}$
274	$\dfrac{s(s+a)}{(s+b)(s^2+\omega^2)}$	$\dfrac{b^2-ab}{b^2+\omega^2}\epsilon^{-bt}+\sqrt{\dfrac{(a^2+\omega^2)}{b^2+\omega^2}}\sin(\omega t+\phi)$ $\phi=\tan^{-1}\left(\dfrac{a}{-\omega}\right)-\tan^{-1}\left(\dfrac{\omega}{b}\right)$

NO.	F(s)	f(t)
275	$\frac{s(s+a)}{(s+b)(s+c)(s^2+\omega^2)}$	$\frac{b^2-ab}{(c-b)(b^2+\omega^2)}\epsilon^{-bt}+\frac{c^2-ac}{(b-c)(c^2+\omega^2)}\epsilon^{-ct}+\sqrt{\frac{(a^2+\omega^2)}{(b^2+\omega^2)(c^2+\omega^2)}}\sin(\omega t+\phi)$ $\phi=\tan^{-1}\left(\frac{a}{-\omega}\right)-\tan^{-1}\left(\frac{\omega}{b}\right)-\tan^{-1}\left(\frac{\omega}{c}\right)$
276	$\frac{s(s+a)}{(s+b)(s+c)(s+d)(s^2+\omega^2)}$	$\frac{b^2-ab}{(c-b)(d-b)(b^2+\omega^2)}\epsilon^{-bt}+\frac{c^2-ac}{(b-c)(d-c)(c^2+\omega^2)}\epsilon^{-ct}+\frac{d^2-ad}{(b-d)(c-d)(d^2+\omega^2)}\epsilon^{-dt}$ $+\sqrt{\frac{(\omega^2+a^2)}{(b^2+\omega^2)(c^2+\omega^2)(d^2+\omega^2)}}\cos(\omega t-\phi)$ $\phi=\tan^{-1}\left(\frac{-\omega}{a}\right)+\tan^{-1}\left(\frac{\omega}{b}\right)+\tan^{-1}\left(\frac{\omega}{c}\right)+\tan^{-1}\left(\frac{\omega}{d}\right)$
277	$\frac{s(s+a)}{(s+b)^2(s^2+\omega^2)}$	$\frac{\sqrt{(a^2+\omega^2)}}{(b^2+\omega^2)}\sin(\omega t+\phi)+\frac{b^2-ab}{b^2+\omega^2}t\epsilon^{-bt}+\frac{a(\omega^2-b^2)-2b\omega^2}{(b^2+\omega^2)^2}\epsilon^{-bt}$ $\phi=\tan^{-1}\left(\frac{a}{-\omega}\right)-2\tan^{-1}\left(\frac{\omega}{b}\right)$
278	$\frac{s(s+a)}{(s+c)(s+b)^2(s^2+\omega^2)}$	$\frac{c^2-ac}{(b-c)^2(c^2+\omega^2)}\epsilon^{-ct}+\frac{1}{(b^2+\omega^2)}\sqrt{\frac{(a^2+\omega^2)}{\omega^2+c^2}}\sin(\omega t+\phi)+\frac{b^2-ab}{(c-b)(b^2+\omega^2)}t\epsilon^{-bt}$ $+\frac{(c-b)(a-2b)(b^2+\omega^2)-(b^2-ab)(\omega^2-2bc+3b^2)}{(c-b)^2(b^2+\omega^2)^2}\epsilon^{-bt}$ $\phi=\tan^{-1}\left(\frac{a}{-\omega}\right)-\tan^{-1}\left(\frac{\omega}{c}\right)-2\tan^{-1}\left(\frac{\omega}{b}\right)$
279	$\frac{s(s+a)}{(s^2+b^2)(s^2+\omega^2)}$	$\frac{\sqrt{(a^2+b^2)}}{(\omega^2-b^2)}\sin(bt+\phi_1)+\frac{\sqrt{(a^2+\omega^2)}}{(b^2-\omega^2)}\sin(\omega t+\phi_2)$ $\phi_1=\tan^{-1}\left(\frac{a}{-b}\right)$, $\phi_2=\tan^{-1}\left(\frac{a}{-\omega}\right)$
280	$\frac{s(s+a)}{(s+c)(s^2+b^2)(s^2+\omega^2)}$	$\frac{c^2-ac}{(c^2+b^2)(c^2+\omega^2)}\epsilon^{-ct}+\frac{1}{(\omega^2-b^2)}\sqrt{\frac{(a^2+b^2)}{c^2+b^2}}\cos(bt-\phi_1)$ $+\frac{1}{(b^2-\omega^2)}\sqrt{\frac{(a^2+\omega^2)}{c^2+\omega^2}}\cos(\omega t-\phi_2)$ $\phi_1=\tan^{-1}\left(\frac{-b}{a}\right)+\tan^{-1}\left(\frac{b}{c}\right)$, $\phi_2=\tan^{-1}\left(\frac{-\omega}{a}\right)+\tan^{-1}\left(\frac{\omega}{c}\right)$
281	$\frac{s(s+a)}{(s^2+\omega^2)^2}$	$-\frac{1}{2\omega}\sqrt{(a^2+\omega^2)}\,t\cos(\omega t+\phi)+\frac{1}{2\omega}\sin\omega t$; $\phi=\tan^{-1}\left(\frac{a}{-\omega}\right)$
282	$\frac{s(s+a)}{(s+b)(s^2+\omega^2)^2}$	$\frac{b^2-ab}{(b^2+\omega^2)^2}\epsilon^{-bt}-\frac{1}{2\omega}\sqrt{\frac{(a^2+\omega^2)}{b^2+\omega^2}}\,t\cos(\omega t+\phi_1)$ $-\frac{(a-b)}{2\omega(b^2+\omega^2)}\sin(\omega t+\phi_2)$ $\phi_1=\tan^{-1}\left(\frac{a}{-\omega}\right)-\tan^{-1}\left(\frac{\omega}{b}\right)$, $\phi_2=-2\tan^{-1}\left(\frac{\omega}{b}\right)$

NO.	F(s)	f(t)
283	$\dfrac{s(s+a)}{(s+c)\left[(s+b)^2+\omega^2\right]}$	$\dfrac{c^2-ac}{(b-c)^2+\omega^2}\epsilon^{-ct}+\dfrac{1}{\omega}\sqrt{\dfrac{(b^2-\omega^2-ab)^2+\omega^2(a-2b)^2}{(b-c)^2+\omega^2}}\,\epsilon^{-bt}\sin(\omega t+\phi)$ $\phi=\tan^{-1}\left[\dfrac{\omega(a-2b)}{b^2-\omega^2-ab}\right]-\tan^{-1}\left(\dfrac{\omega}{c-b}\right)$
284	$\dfrac{s(s+a)}{(s+c)(s+d)\left[(s+b)^2+\omega^2\right]}$	$\dfrac{c^2-ac}{(d-c)\left[(b-c)^2+\omega^2\right]}\epsilon^{-ct}+\dfrac{d^2-ad}{(c-d)\left[(b-d)^2+\omega^2\right]}\epsilon^{-dt}$ $+\dfrac{1}{\omega}\sqrt{\dfrac{(b^2-\omega^2-ab)^2+\omega^2(a-2b)^2}{\left[(d-b)^2+\omega^2\right]\left[(c-b)^2+\omega^2\right]}}\,\epsilon^{-bt}\sin(\omega t+\phi)$ $\phi=\tan^{-1}\left[\dfrac{\omega(a-2b)}{b^2-\omega^2-ab}\right]-\tan^{-1}\left(\dfrac{\omega}{c-b}\right)-\tan^{-1}\left(\dfrac{\omega}{d-b}\right)$
285	$\dfrac{s(s+a)}{(s+c)^2\left[(s+b)^2+\omega^2\right]}$	$\dfrac{c^2-ac}{(b-c)^2+\omega^2}t\epsilon^{-ct}+\dfrac{(a-2c)\left[(b-c)^2+\omega^2\right]-2(b-c)(c^2-ac)}{\left[(b-c)^2+\omega^2\right]^2}\epsilon^{-ct}$ $+\dfrac{\sqrt{(b^2-\omega^2-ab)^2+\omega^2(a-2b)^2}}{\omega\left[(b-c)^2+\omega^2\right]}\epsilon^{-bt}\sin(\omega t+\phi)$ $\phi=\tan^{-1}\left[\dfrac{\omega(a-2b)}{b^2-\omega^2-ab}\right]-2\tan^{-1}\left(\dfrac{\omega}{c-b}\right)$
286	$\dfrac{s(s+a)}{(s+c)(s+d)^2\left[(s+b)^2+\omega^2\right]}$	$\dfrac{c^2-ac}{(d-c)^2\left[(b-c)^2+\omega^2\right]}\epsilon^{-ct}+\dfrac{1}{\omega\left[(d-b)^2+\omega^2\right]}\sqrt{\dfrac{(b^2-\omega^2-ab)^2+\omega^2(a-2b)^2}{(c-b)^2+\omega^2}}\,\epsilon^{-bt}\cos(\omega t-\phi)$ $+\dfrac{d^2-ad}{(c-d)\left[(b-d)^2+\omega^2\right]}t\epsilon^{-dt}+\dfrac{(a-2d)}{(c-d)\left[(b-d)^2+\omega^2\right]}\epsilon^{-dt}$ $-\dfrac{(d^2-ad)\left[(b-d)^2+\omega^2+2(c-d)(b-d)\right]}{(c-d)^2\left[(b-d)^2+\omega^2\right]^2}\epsilon^{-dt}$ $\phi=\tan^{-1}\left[\dfrac{b^2-\omega^2-ab}{\omega(a-2b)}\right]+\tan^{-1}\left(\dfrac{\omega}{c-b}\right)+2\tan^{-1}\left(\dfrac{\omega}{d-b}\right)$
287	$\dfrac{s(s+a)}{(s+c)(s+d)(s+f)\left[(s+b)^2+\omega^2\right]}$	$\dfrac{c^2-ac}{(d-c)(f-c)\left[(b-c)^2+\omega^2\right]}\epsilon^{-ct}+\dfrac{d^2-ad}{(c-d)(f-d)\left[(b-d)^2+\omega^2\right]}\epsilon^{-dt}+\dfrac{f^2-af}{(c-f)(d-f)\left[(b-f)^2+\omega^2\right]}\epsilon^{-ft}$ $+\dfrac{1}{\omega}\sqrt{\dfrac{(b^2-\omega^2-ab)^2+\omega^2(a-2b)^2}{\left[(c-b)^2+\omega^2\right]\left[(d-b)^2+\omega^2\right]\left[(f-d)^2+\omega^2\right]}}\,\epsilon^{-bt}\cos(\omega t-\phi)$ $\phi=\tan^{-1}\left[\dfrac{b^2-\omega^2-ab}{\omega(a-2b)}\right]+\tan^{-1}\left(\dfrac{\omega}{c-b}\right)+\tan^{-1}\left(\dfrac{\omega}{d-b}\right)+\tan^{-1}\left(\dfrac{\omega}{f-b}\right)$
288	$\dfrac{s(s+a)}{(s^2+c^2)\left[(s+b)^2+\omega^2\right]}$	$\sqrt{\dfrac{(a^2+c^2)}{(b^2+\omega^2-c^2)^2+4b^2c^2}}\sin(ct+\phi_1)+\dfrac{1}{\omega}\sqrt{\dfrac{(b^2-\omega^2-ab)^2+\omega^2(a-2b)^2}{(b^2+\omega^2-c^2)^2+4b^2c^2}}\,\epsilon^{-bt}\sin(bt+\phi_2)$ $\phi_1=\tan^{-1}\left(\dfrac{a}{-c}\right)-\tan^{-1}\left(\dfrac{2bc}{b^2+\omega^2-c^2}\right)$ $\phi_2=\tan^{-1}\left[\dfrac{\omega(a-2b)}{b^2-\omega^2-ab}\right]-\tan^{-1}\left(\dfrac{-2b\omega}{c^2+b^2-\omega^2}\right)$

NO.	F(s)	f(t)
289	$\frac{s(s+a)}{(s+d)(s^2+c^2)\left[(s+b)^2+\omega^2\right]}$	$\frac{d^2-ad}{(d^2+c^2)\left[(b-d)^2+\omega^2\right]}\epsilon^{-dt}+\sqrt{\frac{(a^2+c^2)}{(d^2+c^2)\left[(b^2+\omega^2-c^2)^2+4b^2c^2\right]}}\cos(ct-\phi_1)$ $+\frac{1}{\omega}\sqrt{\frac{(b^2-\omega^2-ab)^2+\omega^2(a-2b)^2}{\left[(d-b)^2+\omega^2\right]\left[(b^2+\omega^2-c^2)^2+4b^2c^2\right]}}\epsilon^{-bt}\cos(\omega t-\phi_2)$ $\phi_1=\tan^{-1}\left(\frac{-c}{a}\right)+\tan^{-1}\left(\frac{c}{d}\right)+\tan^{-1}\left(\frac{2bc}{b^2+\omega^2-c^2}\right)$ $\phi_2=\tan^{-1}\left[\frac{b^2-\omega^2-ab}{\omega(a-2b)}\right]+\tan^{-1}\left(\frac{\omega}{d-b}\right)-\tan^{-1}\left(\frac{2b\omega}{b^2-\omega^2+c^2}\right)$
290	$\frac{s(s+a)}{\left[(s+b)^2+\omega^2\right]^2}$	$-\frac{1}{2\omega^2}\sqrt{(b^2-\omega^2-ab)^2+\omega^2(a-2b)^2}\;t\epsilon^{-bt}\cos(\omega t+\phi)$ $+\frac{1}{2\omega^3}\cdot(b^2+\omega^2-ab)\;\epsilon^{-bt}\sin(\omega t)$ $\phi=\tan^{-1}\left[\frac{\omega(a-2b)}{b^2-\omega^2-ab}\right]$
291	$\frac{s(s+a)}{(s+c)\left[(s+b)^2+\omega^2\right]^2}$	$\frac{c^2-ac}{\left[(b-c)^2+\omega^2\right]^2}\epsilon^{-ct}-\frac{1}{2\omega^2}\sqrt{\frac{(b^2-\omega^2-ab)^2+\omega^2(a-2b)^2}{(c-b)^2+\omega^2}}\;t\epsilon^{-bt}\cos(\omega t+\phi_1)$ $+\frac{1}{2\omega^3\left[(c-b)^2+\omega^2\right]}\sqrt{4b^2\omega^2(b-a)^2+\left[\omega^2(a-b-c)+b^2(b-c)+ab(c-b)\right]^2}\;\epsilon^{-bt}\cos(\omega t+\phi_2)$ $\phi_1=\tan^{-1}\left[\frac{\omega(a-2b)}{b^2-\omega^2-ab}\right]-\tan^{-1}\left(\frac{\omega}{c-b}\right)$ $\phi_2=\tan^{-1}\left[\frac{\omega^2(a-b-c)+b^2(b-c)+ab(c-b)}{2b\omega(b-a)}\right]-2\tan^{-1}\left(\frac{\omega}{c-b}\right)$
292	$\frac{s(s+a)}{\left[(s+b)^2+\omega^2\right]\left[(s+c)^2+d^2\right]}$	$\frac{1}{\omega}\sqrt{\frac{(b^2-\omega^2-ab)^2+\omega^2(a-2b)^2}{\left[(c-b)^2+\omega^2-d^2\right]^2+4d^2(c-b)^2}}\epsilon^{-bt}\cos(\omega t-\phi_1)$ $+\frac{1}{d}\sqrt{\frac{(c^2-d^2-ac)^2+d^2(a-2c)^2}{\left[(c-b)^2+\omega^2-d^2\right]^2+4d^2(c-b)^2}}\epsilon^{-ct}\cos(dt-\phi_2)$ $\phi_1=\tan^{-1}\left[\frac{b^2-\omega^2-ab}{\omega(a-2b)}\right]+\tan^{-1}\left[\frac{2\omega(c-b)}{(c-b)^2-\omega^2+d^2}\right]$ $\phi_2=\tan^{-1}\left[\frac{c^2-d^2-ac}{d(a-2c)}\right]+\tan^{-1}\left[\frac{2d(b-c)}{(c-b)^2-d^2+\omega^2}\right]$
293	$\frac{s(s+a)}{(s+f)\left[(s+b)^2+\omega^2\right]\left[(s+c)^2+d^2\right]}$	$\frac{1}{\omega}\sqrt{\frac{(b^2-\omega^2-ab)^2+\omega^2(a-2b)^2}{\left[(f-b)^2+\omega^2\right]\left\{\left[(c-b)^2+\omega^2-d^2\right]^2+4d^2(c-b)^2\right\}}}\epsilon^{-bt}\cos(\omega t-\phi_1)+\frac{f^2-af}{\left[(b-f)^2+\omega^2\right]\left[(c-f)^2+d^2\right]}\epsilon^{-ft}$ $+\frac{1}{d}\sqrt{\frac{(c^2-d^2-ac)^2+d^2(a-2c)^2}{\left[(f-c)^2+d^2\right]\left\{\left[(c-b)^2+\omega^2-d^2\right]^2+4d^2(c-b)^2\right\}}}\epsilon^{-ct}\cos(dt-\phi_2)$ $\phi_1=\tan^{-1}\left[\frac{b^2-\omega^2-ab}{\omega(a-2b)}\right]+\tan^{-1}\left(\frac{\omega}{f-b}\right)+\tan^{-1}\left[\frac{2\omega(c-b)}{(c-b)^2-\omega^2+d^2}\right]$ $\phi_2=\tan^{-1}\left[\frac{c^2-d^2-ac}{d(a-2c)}\right]+\tan^{-1}\left(\frac{d}{f-c}\right)+\tan^{-1}\left[\frac{2d(b-c)}{(c-b)^2+\omega^2-d^2}\right]$

NO.	F(s)	f(t)
294	$\frac{s^2+a_1s+a_0}{s^2(s+b)}$	$\frac{b^2-a_1b+a_0}{b^2}\epsilon^{-bt}+\frac{a_0}{b}t+\frac{a_1b-a_0}{b^2}$
295	$\frac{s^2+a_1s+a_0}{s^3(s+b)}$	$\frac{a_1b-b^2-a_0}{b^3}\epsilon^{-bt}+\frac{a_0}{2b}t^2+\frac{a_1b-a_0}{b^2}t+\frac{b^2-a_1b+a_0}{b^3}$
296	$\frac{s^2+a_1s+a_0}{s(s+b)(s+c)}$	$\frac{a_0}{bc}+\frac{b^2-a_1b+a_0}{b(b-c)}\epsilon^{-bt}+\frac{c^2-a_1c+a_0}{c(c-b)}\epsilon^{-ct}$
297	$\frac{s^2+a_1s+a_0}{s^2(s+b)(s+c)}$	$\frac{a_0}{bc}t+\frac{a_1bc-a_0(b+c)}{b^2c^2}+\frac{b^2-a_1b+a_0}{b^2(c-b)}\epsilon^{-bt}+\frac{c^2-a_1c+a_0}{c^2(b-c)}\epsilon^{-ct}$
298	$\frac{s^2+a_1s+a_0}{(s+b)(s+c)(s+d)}$	$\frac{b^2-a_1b+a_0}{(c-b)(d-b)}\epsilon^{-bt}+\frac{c^2-a_1c+a_0}{(b-c)(d-c)}\epsilon^{-ct}+\frac{d^2-a_1d+a_0}{(b-d)(c-d)}\epsilon^{-dt}$
299	$\frac{s^2+a_1s+a_0}{s(s+b)(s+c)(s+d)}$	$\frac{a_0}{bcd}-\frac{b^2-a_1b+a_0}{b(c-b)(d-b)}\epsilon^{-bt}-\frac{c^2-a_1c+a_0}{c(b-c)(d-c)}\epsilon^{-ct}-\frac{d^2-a_1d+a_0}{d(b-d)(c-d)}\epsilon^{-dt}$
300	$\frac{s^2+a_1s+a_0}{s^2(s+b)(s+c)(s+d)}$	$\frac{a_0}{bcd}t+\frac{a_1}{bcd}-\frac{a_0(bc+bd+cd)}{b^2c^2d^2}+\frac{b^2-a_1b+a_0}{b^2(c-b)(d-b)}\epsilon^{-bt}$ $+\frac{c^2-a_1c+a_0}{c^2(b-c)(d-c)}\epsilon^{-ct}+\frac{d^2-a_1d+a_0}{d^2(b-d)(c-d)}\epsilon^{-dt}$
301	$\frac{s^2+a_1s+a_0}{(s+b)(s+c)(s+d)(s+f)}$	$\frac{b^2-a_1b+a_0}{(c-b)(d-b)(f-b)}\epsilon^{-bt}+\frac{c^2-a_1c+a_0}{(b-c)(d-c)(f-c)}\epsilon^{-ct}+\frac{d^2-a_1d+a_0}{(b-d)(c-d)(f-d)}\epsilon^{-dt}$ $+\frac{f^2-a_1f+a_0}{(b-f)(c-f)(d-f)}\epsilon^{-ft}$
302	$\frac{s^2+a_1s+a_0}{s(s+b)(s+c)(s+d)(s+f)}$	$\frac{a_0}{bcdf}-\frac{b^2-a_1b+a_0}{b(c-b)(d-b)(f-b)}\epsilon^{-bt}-\frac{c^2-a_1c+a_0}{c(b-c)(d-c)(f-c)}\epsilon^{-ct}$ $-\frac{d^2-a_1d+a_0}{d(b-d)(c-d)(f-d)}\epsilon^{-dt}-\frac{f^2-a_1f+a_0}{f(b-f)(c-f)(d-f)}\epsilon^{-ft}$
303	$\frac{s^2+a_1s+a_0}{(s+b)(s+c)(s+d)(s+f)(s+g)}$	$\frac{b^2-a_1b+a_0}{(c-b)(d-b)(f-b)(g-b)}\epsilon^{-bt}+\frac{c^2-a_1c+a_0}{(b-c)(d-c)(f-c)(g-c)}\epsilon^{-ct}+\frac{d^2-a_1d+a_0}{(b-d)(c-d)(f-d)(g-d)}\epsilon^{-dt}$ $+\frac{f^2-a_1f+a_0}{(b-f)(c-f)(d-f)(g-f)}\epsilon^{-ft}+\frac{g^2-a_1g+a_0}{(b-g)(c-g)(d-g)(f-g)}\epsilon^{-gt}$
304	$\frac{s^2+a_1s+a_0}{(s+b)(s+c)(s+d)^2}$	$\frac{b^2-a_1b+a_0}{(c-b)(d-b)^2}\epsilon^{-bt}+\frac{c^2-a_1c+a_0}{(b-c)(d-c)^2}\epsilon^{-ct}+\frac{d^2-a_1d+a_0}{(b-d)(c-d)}t\epsilon^{-dt}$ $+\frac{a_0(2d-b-c)+a_1(bc-d^2)+d(db+dc-2bc)}{(b-d)^2(c-d)^2}\epsilon^{-dt}$
305	$\frac{s^2+a_1s+a_0}{s(s+b)(s+c)(s+d)^2}$	$\frac{a_0}{bcd^2}-\frac{b^2-a_1b+a_0}{b(c-b)(d-b)^2}\epsilon^{-bt}-\frac{c^2-a_1c+a_0}{c(b-c)(d-c)^2}\epsilon^{-ct}-\frac{d^2-a_1d+a_0}{d(b-d)(c-d)}t\epsilon^{-dt}$ $-\left[\frac{a_1-2d}{d(b-d)(c-d)}+\frac{(d^2-a_1d+a_0)[(b-d)(c-d)-d(b+c-2d)]}{d^2(b-d)^2(c-d)^2}\right]\epsilon^{-dt}$

NO.	F(s)	f(t)
306	$\frac{s^2+a_1s+a_0}{(s+b)(s+c)(s+d)(s+f)^2}$	$\frac{b^2-a_1b+a_0}{(c-b)(d-b)(f-b)^2}\epsilon^{-bt}+\frac{c^2-a_1c+a_0}{(b-c)(d-c)(f-c)^2}\epsilon^{-ct}+\frac{d^2-a_1d+a_0}{(b-d)(c-d)(f-d)^2}\epsilon^{-dt}+\frac{f^2-a_1f+a_0}{(b-f)(c-f)(d-f)}t\epsilon^{-ft}+\left[\frac{a_1-2f}{(b-f)(c-f)(d-f)}-\frac{(f^2-a_1f+a_0)[(b-f)(c-f)+(b-f)(d-f)+(c-f)(d-f)]}{(b-f)^2(c-f)^2(d-f)^2}\right]\epsilon^{-ft}$
307	$\frac{s^2+a_1s+a_0}{s(s+b)^2}$	$\frac{a_0}{b^2}-\frac{b^2-a_1b+a_0}{b}t\epsilon^{-bt}+\frac{b^2-a_0}{b^2}\epsilon^{-bt}$
308	$\frac{s^2+a_1s+a_0}{s^2(s+b)^2}$	$\frac{a_0}{b^2}t+\frac{a_1b-2a_0}{b^3}+\frac{b^2-a_1b+a_0}{b^2}t\epsilon^{-bt}+\frac{2a_0-a_1b}{b^3}\epsilon^{-bt}$
309	$\frac{s^2+a_1s+a_0}{(s+b)(s+c)^2}$	$\frac{b^2-a_1b+a_0}{(c-b)^2}\epsilon^{-bt}+\frac{c^2-a_1c+a_0}{(b-c)}t\epsilon^{-ct}+\frac{c^2-2bc+a_1b-a_0}{(b-c)^2}\epsilon^{-ct}$
310	$\frac{s^2+a_1s+a_0}{s(s+b)(s+c)^2}$	$\frac{a_0}{bc^2}-\frac{b^2-a_1b+a_0}{b(c-b)^2}\epsilon^{-bt}+\frac{c^2-a_1c+a_0}{c(c-b)}t\epsilon^{-ct}+\frac{c^2(b-a_1)+a_0(2c-b)}{c^2(c-b)^2}\epsilon^{-ct}$
311	$\frac{s^2+a_1s+a_0}{s^2(s+b)(s+c)^2}$	$\frac{a_0}{bc^2}t+\frac{a_1}{bc^2}-\frac{a_0(c+2b)}{b^2c^3}+\frac{b^2-a_1b+a_0}{b^2(c-b)^2}\epsilon^{-bt}+\frac{c^2-a_1c+a_0}{c^2(b-c)}t\epsilon^{-ct}+\left[\frac{a_1-2c}{c^2(b-c)}+\frac{(c^2-a_1c+a_0)(2b-3c)}{c^3(b-c)^2}\right]\epsilon^{-ct}$
312	$\frac{s^2+a_1s+a_0}{(s+b)^2(s+c)^2}$	$\frac{b^2-a_1b+a_0}{(c-b)^2}t\epsilon^{-bt}+\frac{a_1(b+c)-2(bc+a_0)}{(c-b)^3}\epsilon^{-bt}+\frac{c^2-a_1c+a_0}{(b-c)^2}t\epsilon^{-ct}+\frac{a_1(b+c)-2(bc+a_0)}{(b-c)^3}\epsilon^{-ct}$
313	$\frac{s^2+a_1s+a_0}{s(s+b)^2(s+c)^2}$	$\frac{a_0}{b^2c^2}-\frac{b^2-a_1b+a_0}{b(c-b)^2}t\epsilon^{-bt}-\left[\frac{a_1-2b}{b(c-b)^2}+\frac{(b^2-a_1b+a_0)(c-3b)}{b^2(c-b)^3}\right]\epsilon^{-bt}-\frac{c^2-a_1c+a_0}{c(b-c)^2}t\epsilon^{-ct}-\left[\frac{a_1-2c}{c(b-c)^2}+\frac{(c^2-a_1c+a_0)(b-3c)}{c^2(b-c)^3}\right]\epsilon^{-ct}$
314	$\frac{s^2+a_1s+a_0}{s^2(s+b)^2(s+c)^2}$	$\frac{a_0}{b^2c^2}t+\frac{a_1}{b^2c^2}-\frac{2a_0(b+c)}{b^3c^3}+\frac{b^2-a_1b+a_0}{b^2(c-b)^2}t\epsilon^{-bt}+\left[\frac{a_1-2b}{b^2(c-b)^2}+\frac{2(b^2-a_1b+a_0)(c-2b)}{b^3(c-b)^3}\right]\epsilon^{-bt}+\frac{c^2-a_1c+a_0}{c^2(b-c)^2}t\epsilon^{-ct}+\left[\frac{a_1-2c}{c^2(b-c)^2}+\frac{2(c^2-a_1c+a_0)(b-2c)}{c^3(b-c)^3}\right]\epsilon^{-ct}$
315	$\frac{s^2+a_1s+a_0}{(s+d)(s+b)^2(s+c)^2}$	$\frac{d^2-a_1d+a_0}{(b-d)^2(c-d)^2}\epsilon^{-dt}+\frac{b^2-a_1b+a_0}{(c-b)^2(d-b)}t\epsilon^{-bt}+\left[\frac{a_1-2b}{(c-b)^2(d-b)}-\frac{(b^2-a_1b+a_0)(c+2d-3b)}{(c-b)^3(d-b)^2}\right]\epsilon^{-bt}+\frac{c^2-a_1c+a_0}{(b-c)^2(d-c)}t\epsilon^{-ct}+\left[\frac{a_1-2c}{(b-c)^2(d-c)}-\frac{(c^2-a_1c+a_0)(b+2d-3c)}{(b-c)^3(d-c)^2}\right]\epsilon^{-ct}$

NO.	F(s)	f(t)
316	$\dfrac{s^2+a_1s+a_0}{s^2(s+b)^3}$	$\dfrac{a_0}{b^3}t+\dfrac{a_1b-3a_0}{b^4}+\dfrac{b^2-a_1b+a_0}{2b^2}t^2\epsilon^{-bt}+\dfrac{2a_0-a_1b}{b^3}t\epsilon^{-bt}+\dfrac{3a_0-a_1b}{b^4}\epsilon^{-bt}$
317	$\dfrac{s^2+a_1s+a_0}{s(s^2+\omega^2)}$	$\dfrac{1}{\omega^2}\left[a_0-\sqrt{(a_0-\omega^2)^2+a_1^2\omega^2}\cos(\omega t+\phi)\right];\ \phi=\tan^{-1}\left(\dfrac{a_1\omega}{a_0-\omega^2}\right)$
318	$\dfrac{s^2+a_1s+a_0}{s^2(s^2+\omega^2)}$	$\dfrac{1}{\omega^2}\left[a_0t+a_1-\dfrac{1}{\omega}\sqrt{(a_0-\omega^2)^2+a_1^2\omega^2}\sin(\omega t+\phi)\right];\ \phi=\tan^{-1}\left(\dfrac{a_1\omega}{a_0-\omega^2}\right)$
319	$\dfrac{s^2+a_1s+a_0}{(s+b)(s^2+\omega^2)}$	$\dfrac{b^2-a_1b+a_0}{b^2+\omega^2}\epsilon^{-bt}+\dfrac{1}{\omega}\sqrt{\dfrac{(a_0-\omega^2)^2+a_1^2\omega^2}{b^2+\omega^2}}\sin(\omega t+\phi)$ $\phi=\tan^{-1}\left(\dfrac{a_1\omega}{a_0-\omega^2}\right)-\tan^{-1}\left(\dfrac{\omega}{b}\right)$
320	$\dfrac{s^2+a_1s+a_0}{s(s+b)(s^2+\omega^2)}$	$\dfrac{a_0}{b\omega^2}-\dfrac{b^2-a_1b+a_0}{b(b^2+\omega^2)}\epsilon^{-bt}-\dfrac{1}{\omega^2}\sqrt{\dfrac{(a_0-\omega^2)^2+a_1^2\omega^2}{b^2+\omega^2}}\cos(\omega t+\phi)$ $\phi=\tan^{-1}\left(\dfrac{a_1\omega}{a_0-\omega^2}\right)-\tan^{-1}\left(\dfrac{\omega}{b}\right)$
321	$\dfrac{s^2+a_1s+a_0}{s^2(s+b)(s^2+\omega^2)}$	$\dfrac{a_0}{b\omega^2}t+\dfrac{a_1}{b\omega^2}-\dfrac{a_0}{b^2\omega^2}+\dfrac{b^2-a_1b+a_0}{b^2(b^2+\omega^2)}\epsilon^{-bt}-\dfrac{1}{\omega^3}\sqrt{\dfrac{(a_0-\omega^2)^2+a_1^2\omega^2}{b^2+\omega^2}}\cos(\omega t-\phi)$ $\phi=\tan^{-1}\left(\dfrac{a_0-\omega^2}{a_1\omega}\right)+\tan^{-1}\left(\dfrac{\omega}{b}\right)$
322	$\dfrac{s^2+a_1s+a_0}{(s+b)(s+c)(s^2+\omega^2)}$	$\dfrac{b^2-a_1b+a_0}{(c-b)(b^2+\omega^2)}\epsilon^{-bt}+\dfrac{c^2-a_1c+a_0}{(b-c)(c^2+\omega^2)}\epsilon^{-ct}+\dfrac{1}{\omega}\sqrt{\dfrac{(a_0-\omega^2)^2+a_1^2\omega^2}{(b^2+\omega^2)(c^2+\omega^2)}}\sin(\omega t+\phi)$ $\phi=\tan^{-1}\left(\dfrac{a_1\omega}{a_0-\omega^2}\right)-\tan^{-1}\left(\dfrac{\omega}{b}\right)-\tan^{-1}\left(\dfrac{\omega}{c}\right)$
323	$\dfrac{s^2+a_1s+a_0}{s(s+b)(s+c)(s^2+\omega^2)}$	$\dfrac{a_0}{bc\omega^2}-\dfrac{b^2-a_1b+a_0}{b(c-b)(b^2+\omega^2)}\epsilon^{-bt}-\dfrac{c^2-a_1c+a_0}{c(b-c)(c^2+\omega^2)}\epsilon^{-ct}-\dfrac{1}{\omega^2}\sqrt{\dfrac{(a_0-\omega^2)^2+a_1^2\omega^2}{(b^2+\omega^2)(c^2+\omega^2)}}\cos(\omega t+\phi)$ $\phi=\tan^{-1}\left(\dfrac{a_1\omega}{a_0-\omega^2}\right)-\tan^{-1}\left(\dfrac{\omega}{b}\right)-\tan^{-1}\left(\dfrac{\omega}{c}\right)$
324	$\dfrac{s^2+a_1s+a_0}{(s+b)(s+c)(s+d)(s^2+\omega^2)}$	$\dfrac{b^2-a_1b+a_0}{(c-b)(d-b)(b^2+\omega^2)}\epsilon^{-bt}+\dfrac{c^2-a_1c+a_0}{(b-c)(d-c)(c^2+\omega^2)}\epsilon^{-ct}+\dfrac{d^2-a_1d+a_0}{(b-d)(c-d)(d^2+\omega^2)}\epsilon^{-dt}$ $+\dfrac{1}{\omega}\sqrt{\dfrac{(a_0-\omega^2)^2+a_1^2\omega^2}{(b^2+\omega^2)(c^2+\omega^2)(d^2+\omega^2)}}\cos(\omega t-\phi)$ $\phi=\tan^{-1}\left(\dfrac{a_0-\omega^2}{a_1\omega}\right)+\tan^{-1}\left(\dfrac{\omega}{b}\right)+\tan^{-1}\left(\dfrac{\omega}{c}\right)+\tan^{-1}\left(\dfrac{\omega}{d}\right)$
325	$\dfrac{s^2+a_1s+a_0}{(s+b)^2(s^2+\omega^2)}$	$\dfrac{b^2-a_1b+a_0}{b^2+\omega^2}t\epsilon^{-bt}+\dfrac{2b(a_0-\omega^2)+a_1(\omega^2-b^2)}{(b^2+\omega^2)^2}\epsilon^{-bt}$ $+\dfrac{1}{\omega(b^2+\omega^2)}\sqrt{(a_0-\omega^2)^2+a_1^2\omega^2}\sin(\omega t+\phi)$ $\phi=\tan^{-1}\left(\dfrac{a_1\omega}{a_0-\omega^2}\right)-2\tan^{-1}\left(\dfrac{\omega}{b}\right)$

NO.	F(s)	f(t)
326	$\dfrac{s^2+a_1 s+a_0}{s(s+b)^2(s^2+\omega^2)}$	$\dfrac{a_0}{b^2\omega^2}-\dfrac{b^2-a_1b+a_0}{b(b^2+\omega^2)}t\epsilon^{-bt}-\left[\dfrac{a_1-2b}{b(b^2+\omega^2)}+\dfrac{(b^2-a_1b+a_0)(\omega^2+3b^2)}{b^2(b^2+\omega^2)^2}\right]\epsilon^{-bt}$ $-\dfrac{1}{\omega^2(b^2+\omega^2)}\sqrt{(a_0-\omega^2)^2+a_1^2\omega^2}\ \cos(\omega t+\phi)$ $\phi=\tan^{-1}\left(\dfrac{a_1\omega}{a_0-\omega^2}\right)-2\tan^{-1}\left(\dfrac{\omega}{b}\right)$
327	$\dfrac{s^2+a_1 s+a_0}{(s+c)(s+b)^2(s^2+\omega^2)}$	$\dfrac{c^2-a_1c+a_0}{(c^2+\omega^2)(b-c)^2}\epsilon^{-ct}+\dfrac{1}{\omega(b^2+\omega^2)}\sqrt{\dfrac{(a_0-\omega^2)^2+a_1^2\omega^2}{c^2+\omega^2}}\ \sin(\omega t+\phi)$ $+\left[\dfrac{a_1-2b}{(c-b)(b^2+\omega^2)}-\dfrac{(b^2-a_1b+a_0)(3b^2+\omega^2-2bc)}{(c-b)^2(b^2+\omega^2)^2}\right]\epsilon^{-bt}$ $+\dfrac{b^2-a_1b+a_0}{(c-b)(b^2+\omega^2)}t\epsilon^{-bt}$ $\phi=\tan^{-1}\left(\dfrac{a_1\omega}{a_0-\omega^2}\right)-\tan^{-1}\left(\dfrac{\omega}{c}\right)-2\tan^{-1}\left(\dfrac{\omega}{b}\right)$
328	$\dfrac{s^2+a_1 s+a_0}{(s^2+b^2)(s^2+\omega^2)}$	$\dfrac{1}{b(\omega^2-b^2)}\sqrt{(a_0-b^2)^2+a_1^2b^2}\ \sin(bt+\phi_1)+\dfrac{1}{\omega(b^2-\omega^2)}\sqrt{(a_0-\omega^2)^2+a_1^2\omega^2}\ \sin(\omega t+\phi_2)$ $\phi_1=\tan^{-1}\left(\dfrac{a_1b}{a_0-b^2}\right),\quad \phi_2=\tan^{-1}\left(\dfrac{a_1\omega}{a_0-\omega^2}\right)$
329	$\dfrac{s^2+a_1 s+a_0}{s(s^2+b^2)(s^2+\omega^2)}$	$\dfrac{a_0}{b^2\omega^2}-\dfrac{1}{b^2(\omega^2-b^2)}\sqrt{(a_0-b^2)^2+a_1^2b^2}\cos(bt+\phi_1)$ $-\dfrac{1}{\omega^2(b^2-\omega^2)}\sqrt{(a_0-\omega^2)^2+a_1^2\omega^2}\ \cos(\omega t+\phi_2)$ $\phi_1=\tan^{-1}\left(\dfrac{a_1b}{a_0-b^2}\right),\quad \phi_2=\tan^{-1}\left(\dfrac{a_1\omega}{a_0-\omega^2}\right)$
330	$\dfrac{s^2+a_1 s+a_0}{(s+c)(s^2+b^2)(s^2+\omega^2)}$	$\dfrac{c^2-a_1c+a_0}{(c^2+b^2)(c^2+\omega^2)}\epsilon^{-ct}+\dfrac{1}{b(\omega^2-b^2)}\sqrt{\dfrac{(a_0-b^2)^2+a_1^2b^2}{c^2+b^2}}\ \cos(bt-\phi_1)$ $+\dfrac{1}{\omega(b^2-\omega^2)}\sqrt{\dfrac{(a_0-\omega^2)^2+a_1^2\omega^2}{c^2+\omega^2}}\ \cos(\omega t-\phi_2)$ $\phi_1=\tan^{-1}\left(\dfrac{a_0-b^2}{a_1b}\right)+\tan^{-1}\left(\dfrac{b}{c}\right),\ \phi_2=\tan^{-1}\left(\dfrac{a_0-\omega^2}{a_1\omega}\right)+\tan^{-1}\left(\dfrac{\omega}{c}\right)$
331	$\dfrac{s^2+a_1 s+a_0}{(s^2+\omega^2)^2}$	$\dfrac{1}{2\omega^3}\ (a_0+\omega^2)\ \sin(\omega t)-\dfrac{1}{2\omega^2}\sqrt{(a_0-\omega^2)^2+a_1^2\omega^2}\ t\cos(\omega t+\phi)$ $\phi=\tan^{-1}\left(\dfrac{a_1\omega}{a_0-\omega^2}\right)$
332	$\dfrac{s^2+a_1 s+a_0}{s(s^2+\omega^2)^2}$	$\dfrac{1}{2\omega^3}\left[\dfrac{2a_0}{\omega}-\sqrt{(a_0-\omega^2)^2+a_1^2\omega^2}\ t\sin(\omega t+\phi_1)-\dfrac{1}{\omega}\sqrt{4a_0^2+a_1^2\omega^2}\ \cos(\omega t+\phi_2)\right]$ $\phi_1=\tan^{-1}\left(\dfrac{a_1\omega}{a_0-\omega^2}\right),\quad \phi_2=\tan^{-1}\left(\dfrac{a_1\omega}{2a_0}\right)$

NO.	F(s)	f(t)
333	$\frac{s^2+a_1s+a_0}{s^2(s^2+\omega^2)^2}$	$\frac{a_0}{\omega^4}t+\frac{a_1}{\omega^4}+\frac{1}{2\omega^4}\sqrt{(a_0-\omega^2)^2+a_1^2\omega^2}\;t\cos(\omega t+\phi_1)$ $-\frac{1}{2\omega^5}\sqrt{(3a_0-\omega^2)^2+4a_1^2\omega^2}\;\sin(\omega t+\phi_2)$ $\phi_1=\tan^{-1}\left(\frac{a_1\omega}{a_0-\omega^2}\right),\ \phi_2=\tan^{-1}\left(\frac{2a_1\omega}{3a_0-\omega^2}\right)$
334	$\frac{s^2+a_1s+a_0}{(s+b)(s^2+\omega^2)^2}$	$\frac{b^2-a_1b+a_0}{(b^2+\omega^2)^2}\epsilon^{-bt}-\frac{1}{2\omega^2}\sqrt{\frac{(a_0-\omega^2)^2+a_1^2\omega^2}{b^2+\omega^2}}\;t\cos(\omega t+\phi_1)$ $+\frac{1}{2\omega^3(b^2+\omega^2)}\sqrt{4a_0^2\omega^2+[\omega^2(a_1-b)-a_0b]^2}\;\cos(\omega t+\phi_2)$ $\phi_1=\tan^{-1}\left(\frac{a_1\omega}{a_0-\omega^2}\right)-\tan^{-1}\left(\frac{\omega}{b}\right),\ \phi_2=\tan^{-1}\left[\frac{\omega^2(a_1-b)-ba_0}{2a_0\omega}\right]-2\tan^{-1}\left(\frac{\omega}{b}\right)$
335	$\frac{s^2+a_1s+a_0}{s[(s+b)^2+\omega^2]}$	$\frac{a_0}{b^2+\omega^2}+\frac{1}{\omega}\sqrt{\frac{(b^2-\omega^2-a_1b+a_0)^2+\omega^2(a_1-2b)^2}{b^2+\omega^2}}\;\epsilon^{-bt}\sin(\omega t+\phi)$ $\phi=\tan^{-1}\left[\frac{\omega(a_1-2b)}{b^2-\omega^2-a_1b+a_0}\right]-\tan^{-1}\left(\frac{\omega}{-b}\right)$
336	$\frac{s^2+a_1s+a_0}{s^2[(s+b)^2+\omega^2]}$	$\frac{a_0}{b^2+\omega^2}t-\frac{2a_0b-a_1(b^2+\omega^2)}{(b^2+\omega^2)^2}+\frac{1}{\omega(b^2+\omega^2)}\sqrt{(b^2-\omega^2-a_1b+a_0)^2+\omega^2(a_1-2b)^2}\;\epsilon^{-bt}\cos(\omega t+\phi)$ $\phi=\tan^{-1}\left[\frac{\omega(a_1-2b)}{b^2-\omega^2-a_1b+a_0}\right]-\tan^{-1}\left(\frac{b}{\omega}\right)+\tan^{-1}\left(\frac{\omega}{b}\right)$
337	$\frac{s^2+a_1s+a_0}{(s+c)[(s+b)^2+\omega^2]}$	$\frac{c^2-a_1c+a_0}{(b-c)^2+\omega^2}\epsilon^{-ct}+\frac{1}{\omega}\sqrt{\frac{(b^2-\omega^2-a_1b+a_0)^2+\omega^2(a_1-2b)^2}{(c-b)^2+\omega^2}}\;\epsilon^{-bt}\sin(\omega t+\phi)$ $\phi=\tan^{-1}\left[\frac{\omega(a_1-2b)}{b^2-\omega^2-a_1b+a_0}\right]-\tan^{-1}\left(\frac{\omega}{c-b}\right)$
338	$\frac{s^2+a_1s+a_0}{s(s+c)[(s+b)^2+\omega^2]}$	$\frac{a_0}{c(b^2+\omega^2)}-\frac{c^2-a_1c+a_0}{c[(b-c)^2+\omega^2]}\epsilon^{-ct}-\frac{1}{\omega}\sqrt{\frac{(b^2-\omega^2-a_1b+a_0)^2+\omega^2(a_1-2b)^2}{(b^2+\omega^2)[(c-b)^2+\omega^2]}}\;\epsilon^{-bt}\cos(\omega t+\phi)$ $\phi=\tan^{-1}\left[\frac{\omega(a_1-2b)}{b^2-\omega^2-a_1b+a_0}\right]-\tan^{-1}\left(\frac{b}{\omega}\right)-\tan^{-1}\left(\frac{\omega}{c-b}\right)$
339	$\frac{s^2+a_1s+a_0}{s^2(s+c)[(s+b)^2+\omega^2]}$	$\frac{a_0}{c(b^2+\omega^2)}t+\frac{a_1}{c(b^2+\omega^2)}-\frac{a_0(b^2+\omega^2+2bc)}{c^2(b^2+\omega^2)^2}+\frac{c^2-a_1c+a_0}{c^2[(b-c)^2+\omega^2]}\epsilon^{-ct}$ $+\frac{1}{\omega(b^2+\omega^2)}\sqrt{\frac{(b^2-\omega^2-a_1b+a_0)^2+\omega^2(a_1-2b)^2}{(b-c)^2+\omega^2}}\;\epsilon^{-bt}\cos(\omega t-\phi)$ $\phi=\tan^{-1}\left[\frac{b^2-\omega^2-a_1b+a_0}{\omega(a_1-2b)}\right]+\tan^{-1}\left(\frac{\omega}{c-b}\right)-2\tan^{-1}\left(\frac{\omega}{b}\right)$

NO.	F(s)	f(t)
340	$\frac{s^2+a_1s+a_0}{(s+c)(s+d)[(s+b)^2+\omega^2]}$	$\frac{c^2-a_1c+a_0}{(d-c)[(b-c)^2+\omega^2]}\epsilon^{-ct}+\frac{d^2-a_1d+a_0}{(c-d)[(b-d)^2+\omega^2]}\epsilon^{-dt}+\frac{1}{\omega}\sqrt{\frac{(b^2-\omega^2-a_1b+a_0)^2+\omega^2(a_1-2b)^2}{[(d-b)^2+\omega^2][(c-b)^2+\omega^2]}}\,\epsilon^{-bt}\sin(\omega t+\phi)$ $\phi=\tan^{-1}\left[\frac{\omega(a_1-2b)}{b^2-\omega^2-a_1b+a_0}\right]-\tan^{-1}\left(\frac{\omega}{c-b}\right)-\tan^{-1}\left(\frac{\omega}{d-b}\right)$
341	$\frac{s^2+a_1s+a_0}{s(s+c)(s+d)[(s+b)^2+\omega^2]}$	$\frac{a_0}{cd(b^2+\omega^2)}-\frac{c^2-a_1c+a_0}{c(d-c)[(b-c)^2+\omega^2]}\epsilon^{-ct}-\frac{d^2-a_1d+a_0}{d(c-d)[(b-d)^2+\omega^2]}\epsilon^{-dt}-\frac{1}{\omega}\sqrt{\frac{(b^2-\omega^2-a_1b+a_0)^2+\omega^2(a_1-2b)^2}{(b^2+\omega^2)[(c-b)^2+\omega^2][(d-b)^2+\omega^2]}}\,\epsilon^{-bt}\cos(\omega t+\phi)$ $\phi=\tan^{-1}\left[\frac{\omega(a_1-2b)}{b^2-\omega^2-a_1b+a_0}\right]-\tan^{-1}\left(\frac{b}{\omega}\right)-\tan^{-1}\left(\frac{\omega}{c-b}\right)-\tan^{-1}\left(\frac{\omega}{d-b}\right)$
342	$\frac{s^2+a_1s+a_0}{(s+c)^2[(s+b)^2+\omega^2]}$	$\frac{c^2-a_1c+a_0}{(b-c)^2+\omega^2}t\epsilon^{-ct}+\left[\frac{a_1-2c}{(b-c)^2+\omega^2}-\frac{2(b-c)(c^2-a_1c+a_0)}{[(b-c)^2+\omega^2]^2}\right]\epsilon^{-ct}+\frac{1}{\omega[(c-b)^2+\omega^2]}\sqrt{(b^2-\omega^2-a_1b+a_0)^2+\omega^2(a_1-2b)^2}\,\epsilon^{-bt}\sin(\omega t+\phi)$ $\phi=\tan^{-1}\left[\frac{\omega(a_1-2b)}{b^2-\omega^2-a_1b+a_0}\right]-2\tan^{-1}\left(\frac{\omega}{c-b}\right)$
343	$\frac{s^2+a_1s+a_0}{s(s+c)^2[(s+b)^2+\omega^2]}$	$\frac{a_0}{c^2(b^2+\omega^2)}-\frac{c^2-a_1c+a_0}{c[(b-c)^2+\omega^2]}t\epsilon^{-ct}-\left[\frac{a_1-2c}{c[(b-c)^2+\omega^2]}+\frac{(c^2-a_1c+a_0)[(b-c)^2+\omega^2-2bc+2c^2]}{c^2[(b-c)^2+\omega^2]^2}\right]\epsilon^{-ct}-\frac{1}{\omega[(c-b)^2+\omega^2]}\sqrt{\frac{(b^2-\omega^2-a_1b+a_0)^2+\omega^2(a_1-2b)^2}{b^2+\omega^2}}\,\epsilon^{-bt}\cos(\omega t+\phi)$ $\phi=\tan^{-1}\left[\frac{\omega(a_1-2b)}{b^2-\omega^2-a_1b+a_0}\right]-\tan^{-1}\left(\frac{b}{\omega}\right)-2\tan^{-1}\left(\frac{\omega}{c-b}\right)$
344	$\frac{s^2+a_1s+a_0}{(s+d)(s+c)^2[(s+b)^2+\omega^2]}$	$\frac{d^2-a_1d+a_0}{(c-d)^2[(b-d)^2+\omega^2]}\epsilon^{-dt}+\frac{1}{\omega[(c-b)^2+\omega^2]}\sqrt{\frac{(b^2-\omega^2-a_1b+a_0)^2+\omega^2(a_1-2b)^2}{(d-b)^2+\omega^2}}\,\epsilon^{-bt}\cos(\omega t-\phi)$ $+\frac{c^2-a_1c+a_0}{(d-c)[(b-c)^2+\omega^2]}t\epsilon^{-ct}+\left[\frac{a_1-2c}{(d-c)[(b-c)^2+\omega^2]}-\frac{(c^2-a_1c+a_0)[(b-c)^2+\omega^2+2(d-c)(b-c)]}{(d-c)^2[(b-c)^2+\omega^2]^2}\right]\epsilon^{-ct}$ $\phi=\tan^{-1}\left[\frac{b^2-\omega^2-a_1b+a_0}{\omega(a_1-2b)}\right]+\tan^{-1}\left(\frac{\omega}{d-b}\right)+2\tan^{-1}\left(\frac{\omega}{c-b}\right)$
345	$\frac{s^2+a_1s+a_0}{(s+c)(s+d)(s+f)[(s+b)^2+\omega^2]}$	$\frac{c^2-a_1c+a_0}{(d-c)(f-c)[(b-c)^2+\omega^2]}\epsilon^{-ct}+\frac{d^2-a_1d+a_0}{(c-d)(f-d)[(b-d)^2+\omega^2]}\epsilon^{-dt}+\frac{f^2-a_1f+a_0}{(c-f)(d-f)[(b-f)^2+\omega^2]}\epsilon^{-ft}$ $+\frac{1}{\omega}\sqrt{\frac{(b^2-\omega^2-a_1b+a_0)^2+\omega^2(a_1-2b)^2}{[(c-b)^2+\omega^2][(d-b)^2+\omega^2][(f-b)^2+\omega^2]}}\,\epsilon^{-bt}\cos(\omega t-\phi)$ $\phi=\tan^{-1}\left[\frac{b^2-\omega^2-a_1b+a_0}{\omega(a_1-2b)}\right]+\tan^{-1}\left(\frac{\omega}{c-b}\right)+\tan^{-1}\left(\frac{\omega}{d-b}\right)+\tan^{-1}\left(\frac{\omega}{f-b}\right)$

NO.	F(s)	f(t)
346	$\frac{s^2+a_1s+a_0}{(s^2+c^2)\left[(s+b)^2+\omega^2\right]}$	$\frac{1}{c}\sqrt{\frac{(a_0-c^2)^2+a_1^2c^2}{(b^2+\omega^2-c^2)^2+4b^2c^2}}\sin(ct+\phi_1)+\frac{1}{\omega}\sqrt{\frac{(b^2-\omega^2-a_1b+a_0)^2+\omega^2(a_1-2b)^2}{(b^2+\omega^2-c^2)^2+4b^2c^2}}\,\epsilon^{-bt}\sin(\omega t+\phi_2)$ $\phi_1=\tan^{-1}\left(\frac{a_1c}{a_0-c^2}\right)-\tan^{-1}\left(\frac{2bc}{b^2+\omega^2-c^2}\right)$ $\phi_2=\tan^{-1}\left[\frac{\omega(a_1-2b)}{b^2-\omega^2-a_1b+a_0}\right]-\tan^{-1}\left(\frac{-2b\omega}{b^2-\omega^2+c^2}\right)$
347	$\frac{s^2+a_1s+a_0}{s(s^2+c^2)\left[(s+b)^2+\omega^2\right]}$	$\frac{a_0}{c^2(b^2+\omega^2)}-\frac{1}{c^2}\sqrt{\frac{(a_0-c^2)^2+a_1^2c^2}{(b^2+\omega^2-c^2)^2+4b^2c^2}}\cos(ct+\phi_1)$ $-\frac{1}{\omega}\sqrt{\frac{(b^2-\omega^2-a_1b+a_0)^2+\omega^2(a_1-2b)^2}{(b^2+\omega^2)\left[(b^2+\omega^2-c^2)^2+4b^2c^2\right]}}\,\epsilon^{-bt}\cos(\omega t+\phi_2)$ $\phi_1=\tan^{-1}\left(\frac{a_1c}{a_0-c^2}\right)-\tan^{-1}\left(\frac{2bc}{b^2+\omega^2-c^2}\right)$ $\phi_2=\tan^{-1}\left[\frac{\omega(a_1-2b)}{b^2-\omega^2-a_1b+a_0}\right]-\tan^{-1}\left(\frac{b^2-\omega^2+c^2}{2b\omega}\right)+\tan^{-1}\left(\frac{\omega}{b}\right)$
348	$\frac{s^2+a_1s+a_0}{(s+d)(s^2+c^2)\left[(s+b)^2+\omega^2\right]}$	$\frac{d^2-a_1d+a_0}{(d^2+c^2)\left[(b-d)^2+\omega^2\right]}\,\epsilon^{-dt}+\frac{1}{c}\sqrt{\frac{(a_0-c^2)^2+a_1^2c^2}{(d^2+c^2)\left[(b^2+\omega^2-c^2)^2+4b^2c^2\right]}}\cos(ct-\phi_1)$ $+\frac{1}{\omega}\sqrt{\frac{(b^2-\omega^2-a_1b+a_0)^2+\omega^2(a_1-2b)^2}{\left[(d-b)^2+\omega^2\right]\left[(b^2+\omega^2-c^2)^2+4b^2c^2\right]}}\,\epsilon^{-bt}\cos(\omega t-\phi_2)$ $\phi_1=\tan^{-1}\left(\frac{a_0-c^2}{a_1c}\right)+\tan^{-1}\left(\frac{c}{d}\right)+\tan^{-1}\left(\frac{2bc}{b^2+\omega^2-c^2}\right)$ $\phi_2=\tan^{-1}\left[\frac{b^2-\omega^2-a_1b+a_0}{\omega(a_1-2b)}\right]+\tan^{-1}\left(\frac{\omega}{d-b}\right)-\tan^{-1}\left(\frac{2b\omega}{b^2-\omega^2+c^2}\right)$
349	$\frac{s^2+a_1s+a_0}{\left[(s+b)^2+\omega^2\right]^2}$	$\frac{1}{2\omega^3}\cdot\left[a_0-a_1b+b^2+\omega^2\right]\cdot\epsilon^{-bt}\sin(\omega t)$ $-\frac{1}{2\omega^2}\sqrt{(b^2-\omega^2-a_1b+a_0)^2+\omega^2(a_1-2b)^2}\;t\epsilon^{-bt}\cos(\omega t+\phi)$ $\phi=\tan^{-1}\left[\frac{\omega(a_1-2b)}{b^2-\omega^2-a_1b+a_0}\right]$
350	$\frac{s^2+a_1s+a_0}{s\left[(s+b)^2+\omega^2\right]^2}$	$\frac{a_0}{(b^2+\omega^2)^2}-\frac{1}{2\omega^2}\sqrt{\frac{(b^2-\omega^2-a_1b+a_0)^2+\omega^2(a_1-2b)^2}{b^2+\omega^2}}\;t\epsilon^{-bt}\cos(\omega t+\phi_1)$ $+\frac{1}{2\omega^3(b^2+\omega^2)}\sqrt{4\omega^2\left[b(b-a_1)+a_0\right]^2+\left[b(a_0-a_1b+b^2)+\omega^2(a_1-b)\right]^2}\,\epsilon^{-bt}\cos(\omega t+\phi_2)$ $\phi_1=\tan^{-1}\left[\frac{\omega(a_1-2b)}{b^2-\omega^2-a_1b+a_0}\right]-\tan^{-1}\left(\frac{\omega}{-b}\right)$ $\phi_2=\tan^{-1}\left[\frac{b(a_0-a_1b+b^2)+\omega^2(a_1-b)}{2\omega\left[b(b-a_1)+a_0\right]}\right]-2\tan^{-1}\left(\frac{\omega}{-b}\right)$

NO.	F(s)	f(t)
351	$\dfrac{s^2+a_1s+a_0}{(s+c)\left[(s+b)^2+\omega^2\right]^2}$	$\dfrac{c^2-a_1c+a_0}{\left[(b-c)^2+\omega^2\right]^2}\epsilon^{-ct}-\dfrac{1}{2\omega^2}\sqrt{\dfrac{(b^2-\omega^2-a_1b+a_0)^2+\omega^2(a_1-2b)^2}{(c-b)^2+\omega^2}}\,t\epsilon^{-bt}\cos(\omega t+\phi_1)$ $+\dfrac{1}{2\omega^3\left[(c-b)^2+\omega^2\right]}\sqrt{4\omega^2\left[b(b-a_1)+a_0\right]^2+\left[(b-c)(a_0-a_1b+b^2)+\omega^2(a_1-b-c)\right]^2}\,\epsilon^{-bt}\cos(\omega t+\phi_2)$ $\phi_1=\tan^{-1}\left[\dfrac{\omega(a_1-2b)}{b^2-\omega^2-a_1b+a_0}\right]-\tan^{-1}\left(\dfrac{\omega}{c-b}\right)$ $\phi_2=\tan^{-1}\left[\dfrac{(b-c)(a_0-a_1b+b^2)+\omega^2(a_1-b-c)}{2\omega\left[b(b-a_1)+a_0\right]}\right]-2\tan^{-1}\left(\dfrac{\omega}{c-b}\right)$
352	$\dfrac{s^2+a_1s+a_0}{\left[(s+c)^2+d^2\right]\left[(s+b)^2+\omega^2\right]}$	$\dfrac{1}{d}\sqrt{\dfrac{(c^2-d^2-a_1c+a_0)^2+d^2(a_1-2c)^2}{\left[(b-c)^2+d^2-\omega^2\right]^2+4\omega^2(b-c)^2}}\,\epsilon^{-ct}\cos(dt-\phi_1)$ $+\dfrac{1}{\omega}\sqrt{\dfrac{(b^2-\omega^2-a_1b+a_0)^2+\omega^2(a_1-2b)^2}{\left[(b-c)^2+d^2-\omega^2\right]^2+4\omega^2(b-c)^2}}\,\epsilon^{-bt}\cos(\omega t-\phi_2)$ $\phi_1=\tan^{-1}\left[\dfrac{c^2-d^2-a_1c+a_0}{d(a_1-2c)}\right]+\tan^{-1}\left[\dfrac{2d(b-c)}{(b-c)^2-d^2+\omega^2}\right]$ $\phi_2=\tan^{-1}\left[\dfrac{b^2-\omega^2-a_1b+a_0}{\omega(a_1-2b)}\right]+\tan^{-1}\left[\dfrac{2\omega(c-b)}{(b-c)^2-\omega^2+d^2}\right]$
353	$\dfrac{s^2+a_1s+a_0}{s\left[(s+c)^2+d^2\right]\left[(s+b)^2+\omega^2\right]}$	$\dfrac{a_0}{(c^2+d^2)(b^2+\omega^2)}-\dfrac{1}{d}\sqrt{\dfrac{(c^2-d^2-a_1c+a_0)^2+d^2(a_1-2c)^2}{(c^2+d^2)\left\{\left[(b-c)^2+d^2-\omega^2\right]^2+4\omega^2(b-c)^2\right\}}}\,\epsilon^{-ct}\cos(dt+\phi_1)$ $-\dfrac{1}{\omega}\sqrt{\dfrac{(b^2-\omega^2-a_1b+a_0)^2+\omega^2(a_1-2b)^2}{(b^2+\omega^2)\left\{\left[(b-c)^2+d^2-\omega^2\right]^2+4\omega^2(b-c)^2\right\}}}\,\epsilon^{-bt}\cos(\omega t+\phi_2)$ $\phi_1=\tan^{-1}\left[\dfrac{d(a_1-2c)}{c^2-d^2-a_1c+a_0}\right]-\tan^{-1}\left(\dfrac{c}{d}\right)-\tan^{-1}\left[\dfrac{2d(b-c)}{(b-c)^2-d^2+\omega^2}\right]$ $\phi_2=\tan^{-1}\left[\dfrac{\omega(a_1-2b)}{b^2-\omega^2-a_1b+a_0}\right]-\tan^{-1}\left(\dfrac{b}{\omega}\right)-\tan^{-1}\left[\dfrac{2\omega(c-b)}{(b-c)^2+d^2-\omega^2}\right]$
354	$\dfrac{s^2+a_1s+a_0}{(s+f)\left[(s+b)^2+\omega^2\right]\left[(s+c)^2+d^2\right]}$	$\dfrac{f^2-a_1f+a_0}{\left[(b-f)^2+\omega^2\right]\left[(c-f)^2+d^2\right]}\epsilon^{-ft}+\dfrac{1}{\omega}\sqrt{\dfrac{(b^2-\omega^2-a_1b+a_0)^2+\omega^2(a_1-2b)^2}{\left[(f-b)^2+\omega^2\right]\left\{\left[(c-b)^2+\omega^2-d^2\right]^2+4d^2(c-b)^2\right\}}}\,\epsilon^{-bt}\cos(\omega t-\phi_1)$ $+\dfrac{1}{d}\sqrt{\dfrac{(c^2-d^2-a_1c+a_0)^2+d^2(a_1-2c)^2}{\left[(f-c)^2+d^2\right]\left\{\left[(c-b)^2+\omega^2-d^2\right]^2+4d^2(c-b)^2\right\}}}\,\epsilon^{-ct}\cos(dt-\phi_2)$ $\phi_1=\tan^{-1}\left[\dfrac{b^2-\omega^2-a_1b+a_0}{\omega(a_1-2b)}\right]+\tan^{-1}\left(\dfrac{\omega}{f-b}\right)+\tan^{-1}\left[\dfrac{2\omega(c-b)}{(c-b)^2+d^2-\omega^2}\right]$ $\phi_2=\tan^{-1}\left[\dfrac{c^2-d^2-a_1c+a_0}{d\,(a_1-2c)}\right]+\tan^{-1}\left(\dfrac{d}{f-c}\right)+\tan^{-1}\left[\dfrac{2d(b-c)}{(c-b)^2+\omega^2-d^2}\right]$
355	$\dfrac{s^3}{(s+b)(s+c)(s+d)(s+f)}$	$\dfrac{b^3}{(b-c)(d-b)(f-b)}\epsilon^{-bt}+\dfrac{c^3}{(c-b)(d-c)(f-c)}\epsilon^{-ct}+\dfrac{d^3}{(d-b)(c-d)(f-d)}\epsilon^{-dt}+\dfrac{f^3}{(f-b)(c-f)(d-f)}\epsilon^{-ft}$
356	$\dfrac{s^3}{(s+b)(s+c)(s+d)(s+f)(s+g)}$	$\dfrac{b^3}{(b-c)(d-b)(f-b)(g-b)}\epsilon^{-bt}+\dfrac{c^3}{(c-b)(d-c)(f-c)(g-c)}\epsilon^{-ct}+\dfrac{d^3}{(d-b)(c-d)(f-d)(g-d)}\epsilon^{-dt}$ $+\dfrac{f^3}{(f-b)(c-f)(d-f)(g-f)}\epsilon^{-ft}+\dfrac{g^3}{(g-b)(c-g)(d-g)(f-g)}\epsilon^{-gt}$

NO.	F(s)	f(t)
357	$\frac{s^3}{(s+b)(s+c)(s+d)^2}$	$\frac{b^3}{(b-c)(d-b)^2}\epsilon^{-bt}+\frac{c^3}{(c-b)(d-c)^2}\epsilon^{-ct}+\frac{d^3}{(d-b)(c-d)}t\epsilon^{-dt}+\frac{d^2[d^2-2d(b+c)+3bc]}{(b-d)^2(c-d)^2}\epsilon^{-dt}$
358	$\frac{s^3}{(s+b)(s+c)(s+d)(s+f)^2}$	$\frac{b^3}{(b-c)(d-b)(f-b)^2}\epsilon^{-bt}+\frac{c^3}{(c-b)(d-c)(f-c)^2}\epsilon^{-ct}+\frac{d^3}{(d-b)(c-d)(f-d)^2}\epsilon^{-dt}+\frac{f^3}{(f-b)(c-f)(d-f)}t\epsilon^{-ft}$ $+\left[\frac{3f^2}{(b-f)(c-f)(d-f)}+\frac{f^3[(b-f)(c-f)+(b-f)(d-f)+(c-f)(d-f)]}{(b-f)^2(c-f)^2(d-f)^2}\right]\epsilon^{-ft}$
359	$\frac{s^3}{(s+b)^2(s+c)^2}$	$-\frac{b^3}{(c-b)^2}t\epsilon^{-bt}+\frac{b^2(3c-b)}{(c-b)^3}\epsilon^{-bt}-\frac{c^3}{(b-c)^2}t\epsilon^{-ct}+\frac{c^2(3b-c)}{(b-c)^3}\epsilon^{-ct}$
360	$\frac{s^3}{(s+d)(s+b)^2(s+c)^2}$	$-\frac{d^3}{(b-d)^2(c-d)^2}\epsilon^{-dt}+\frac{b^3}{(c-b)^2(b-d)}t\epsilon^{-bt}+\left[\frac{3b^2}{(c-b)^2(d-b)}+\frac{b^3(c+2d-3b)}{(c-b)^3(d-b)^2}\right]\epsilon^{-bt}$ $+\frac{c^3}{(b-c)^2(c-d)}t\epsilon^{-ct}+\left[\frac{3c^2}{(b-c)^2(d-c)}+\frac{c^3(b+2d-3c)}{(b-c)^3(d-c)^2}\right]\epsilon^{-ct}$
361	$\frac{s^3}{(s+b)(s+c)(s^2+\omega^2)}$	$\frac{b^3}{(b-c)(b^2+\omega^2)}\epsilon^{-bt}+\frac{c^3}{(c-b)(c^2+\omega^2)}\epsilon^{-ct}-\frac{\omega^2}{\sqrt{(b^2+\omega^2)(c^2+\omega^2)}}\sin(\omega t+\phi)$ $\phi=\tan^{-1}\left(\frac{c}{\omega}\right)-\tan^{-1}\left(\frac{\omega}{b}\right)$
362	$\frac{s^3}{(s+b)(s+c)(s+d)(s^2+\omega^2)}$	$\frac{b^3}{(b-c)(d-b)(b^2+\omega^2)}\epsilon^{-bt}+\frac{c^3}{(c-b)(d-c)(c^2+\omega^2)}\epsilon^{-ct}+\frac{d^3}{(d-b)(c-d)(d^2+\omega^2)}\epsilon^{-dt}$ $-\frac{\omega^2}{\sqrt{(b^2+\omega^2)(c^2+\omega^2)(d^2+\omega^2)}}\cos(\omega t-\phi)$ $\phi=\tan^{-1}\left(\frac{\omega}{b}\right)+\tan^{-1}\left(\frac{\omega}{c}\right)+\tan^{-1}\left(\frac{\omega}{d}\right)$
363	$\frac{s^3}{(s+b)^2(s^2+\omega^2)}$	$-\frac{b^3}{b^2+\omega^2}t\epsilon^{-bt}+\frac{b^2(b^2+3\omega^2)}{(b^2+\omega^2)^2}\epsilon^{-bt}-\frac{\omega^2}{(b^2+\omega^2)}\sin(\omega t+\phi)$ $\phi=\tan^{-1}\left(\frac{b}{\omega}\right)-\tan^{-1}\left(\frac{\omega}{b}\right)$
364	$\frac{s^3}{(s+c)(s+b)^2(s^2+\omega^2)}$	$-\frac{c^3}{(b-c)^2(c^2+\omega^2)}\epsilon^{-ct}-\frac{1}{(b^2+\omega^2)}\cdot\frac{\omega^2}{\sqrt{c^2+\omega^2}}\cos(\omega t-\phi)$ $+\frac{b^3}{(b-c)(b^2+\omega^2)}t\epsilon^{-bt}+\left[\frac{3b^2}{(c-b)(b^2+\omega^2)}+\frac{b^3(\omega^2+3b^2-2bc)}{(c-b)^2(b^2+\omega^2)^2}\right]\epsilon^{-bt}$ $\phi=\tan^{-1}\left(\frac{\omega}{c}\right)+2\tan^{-1}\left(\frac{\omega}{b}\right)$
365	$\frac{s^3}{(s^2+b^2)(s^2+\omega^2)}$	$-\frac{\omega^2}{(b^2-\omega^2)}\cos(\omega t)-\frac{b^2}{(\omega^2-b^2)}\cos(bt)$
366	$\frac{s^3}{(s+c)(s^2+b^2)(s^2+\omega^2)}$	$-\frac{\omega^2}{(b^2-\omega^2)\sqrt{c^2+\omega^2}}\cos(\omega t-\phi_1)-\frac{b^2}{(\omega^2-b^2)\sqrt{c^2+b^2}}\cos(bt-\phi_2)-\frac{c^3}{(c^2+\omega^2)(c^2+b^2)}\epsilon^{-bt}$ $\phi_1=\tan^{-1}\left(\frac{\omega}{c}\right),\ \phi_2=\tan^{-1}\left(\frac{b}{c}\right)$

NO.	F(s)	f(t)
367	$\dfrac{s^3}{(s^2+\omega^2)^2}$	$\cos(\omega t)-\dfrac{\omega}{2}\,t\sin(\omega t)$
368	$\dfrac{s^3}{(s+b)(s^2+\omega^2)^2}$	$-\dfrac{b^3}{(b^2+\omega^2)^2}\epsilon^{-bt}-\dfrac{\omega}{2\sqrt{b^2+\omega^2}}\,t\sin(\omega t+\phi_1)$ $+\dfrac{1}{2\omega^3(b^2+\omega^2)}\sqrt{\omega^6(4b^2+\omega^2)}\;\cos(\omega t+\phi_2)$ $\phi_1=-\tan^{-1}\left(\dfrac{\omega}{b}\right),\ \phi_2=\tan^{-1}\left(\dfrac{\omega}{2b}\right)-2\tan^{-1}\left(\dfrac{\omega}{b}\right)$
369	$\dfrac{s^3}{(s+c)(s+d)\left[(s+b)^2+\omega^2\right]}$	$\dfrac{c^3}{(c-d)\left[(b-c)^2+\omega^2\right]}\epsilon^{-ct}+\dfrac{d^3}{(d-c)\left[(b-d)^2+\omega^2\right]}\epsilon^{-dt}$ $+\dfrac{1}{\omega}\sqrt{\dfrac{b^2(3\omega^2-b^2)^2+\omega^2(3b^2-\omega^2)^2}{\left[(c-b)^2+\omega^2\right]\left[(d-b)^2+\omega^2\right]}}\;\epsilon^{-bt}\cos(\omega t-\phi)$ $\phi=\tan^{-1}\left[\dfrac{b(3\omega^2-b^2)}{\omega(3b^2-\omega^2)}\right]+\tan^{-1}\left(\dfrac{\omega}{c-b}\right)+\tan^{-1}\left(\dfrac{\omega}{d-b}\right)$
370	$\dfrac{s^3}{(s+c)^2\left[(s+b)^2+\omega^2\right]}$	$\dfrac{1}{\omega\left[(c-b)^2+\omega^2\right]}\sqrt{b^2(3\omega^2-b^2)^2+\omega^2(3b^2-\omega^2)^2}\;\epsilon^{-bt}\cos(\omega t-\phi)$ $-\dfrac{c^3}{(b-c)^2+\omega^2}\,t\epsilon^{-ct}+\dfrac{c^2(c^2+3b^2+3\omega^2-4bc)}{\left[(b-c)^2+\omega^2\right]^2}\epsilon^{-ct}$ $\phi=\tan^{-1}\left[\dfrac{b(3\omega^2-b^2)}{\omega(3b^2-\omega^2)}\right]+2\tan^{-1}\left(\dfrac{\omega}{c-b}\right)$
371	$\dfrac{s^3}{(s+c)(s+d)^2\left[(s+b)^2+\omega^2\right]}$	$\dfrac{d^3}{(d-c)\left[(b-d)^2+\omega^2\right]}t\epsilon^{-dt}+\left[\dfrac{3d^2}{(c-d)\left[(b-d)^2+\omega^2\right]}+\dfrac{d^3\left[(b-d)^2+\omega^2+2(c-d)(b-d)\right]}{(c-d)^2\left[(b-d)^2+\omega^2\right]^2}\right]\epsilon^{-dt}$ $-\dfrac{c^3}{(d-c)^2\left[(b-c)^2+\omega^2\right]}\epsilon^{-ct}+\dfrac{1}{\omega\left[(d-b)^2+\omega^2\right]}\sqrt{\dfrac{b^2(3\omega^2-b^2)^2+\omega^2(3b^2-\omega^2)^2}{(c-b)^2+\omega^2}}\;\epsilon^{-bt}\cos(\omega t-\phi)$ $\phi=\tan^{-1}\left[\dfrac{b(3\omega^2-b^2)}{\omega(3b^2-\omega^2)}\right]+\tan^{-1}\left(\dfrac{\omega}{c-b}\right)+2\tan^{-1}\left(\dfrac{\omega}{d-b}\right)$
372	$\dfrac{s^3}{(s+c)(s+d)(s+f)\left[(s+b)^2+\omega^2\right]}$	$\dfrac{c^3}{(c-d)(f-c)\left[(b-c)^2+\omega^2\right]}\epsilon^{-ct}+\dfrac{d^3}{(d-c)(f-d)\left[(b-d)^2+\omega^2\right]}\epsilon^{-dt}+\dfrac{f^3}{(f-c)(d-f)\left[(b-f)^2+\omega^2\right]}\epsilon^{-ft}$ $+\dfrac{1}{\omega}\sqrt{\dfrac{b^2(3\omega^2-b^2)^2+\omega^2(3b^2-\omega^2)^2}{\left[(c-b)^2+\omega^2\right]\left[(d-b)^2+\omega^2\right]\left[(f-b)^2+\omega^2\right]}}\;\epsilon^{-bt}\cos(\omega t-\phi)$ $\phi=\tan^{-1}\left[\dfrac{b(3\omega^2-b^2)}{\omega(3b^2-\omega^2)}\right]+\tan^{-1}\left(\dfrac{\omega}{c-b}\right)+\tan^{-1}\left(\dfrac{\omega}{d-b}\right)+\tan^{-1}\left(\dfrac{\omega}{f-b}\right)$
373	$\dfrac{s^3}{(s^2+c^2)\left[(s+b)^2+\omega^2\right]}$	$\dfrac{-c^2}{\sqrt{(b^2+\omega^2-c^2)^2+4b^2c^2}}\cos(ct-\phi_1)+\dfrac{1}{\omega}\sqrt{\dfrac{b^2(3\omega^2-b^2)^2+\omega^2(3b^2-\omega^2)^2}{(b^2+\omega^2-c^2)^2+4b^2c^2}}\;\epsilon^{-bt}\cos(\omega t-\phi_2)$ $\phi_1=\tan^{-1}\left(\dfrac{2bc}{b^2+\omega^2-c^2}\right)$ $\phi_2=\tan^{-1}\left[\dfrac{b(3\omega^2-b^2)}{\omega(3b^2-\omega^2)}\right]-\tan^{-1}\left(\dfrac{2b\omega}{b^2-\omega^2+c^2}\right)$

NO.	F(s)	f(t)
374	$\dfrac{s^3}{(s+d)(s^2+c^2)\left[(s+b)^2+\omega^2\right]}$	$-\dfrac{d^3}{(d^2+c^2)\left[(b-d)^2+\omega^2\right]}\epsilon^{-dt}-\dfrac{c^2}{\sqrt{(d^2+c^2)\left[(b^2+\omega^2-c^2)^2+4b^2c^2\right]}}\cos(ct-\phi_1)$ $+\dfrac{1}{\omega}\sqrt{\dfrac{b^2(3\omega^2-b^2)^2+\omega^2(3b^2-\omega^2)^2}{\left[(d-b)^2+\omega^2\right]\left[(b^2+\omega^2-c^2)^2+4b^2c^2\right]}}\,\epsilon^{-bt}\cos(\omega t-\phi_2)$ $\phi_1=\tan^{-1}\left(\dfrac{c}{d}\right)+\tan^{-1}\left(\dfrac{2bc}{b^2+\omega^2-c^2}\right)$ $\phi_2=\tan^{-1}\left[\dfrac{b(3\omega^2-b^2)}{\omega(3b^2-\omega^2)}\right]+\tan^{-1}\left(\dfrac{\omega}{d-b}\right)-\tan^{-1}\left(\dfrac{2b\omega}{b^2-\omega^2+c^2}\right)$
375	$\dfrac{s^3}{\left[(s+b)^2+\omega^2\right]^2}$	$\dfrac{1}{2\omega^3}\sqrt{4\omega^6+b^2(b^2+3\omega^2)^2}\,\epsilon^{-bt}\cos(\omega t-\phi_1)$ $-\dfrac{1}{2\omega^2}\sqrt{b^2(3\omega^2-b^2)^2+\omega^2(3b^2-\omega^2)^2}\,t\epsilon^{-bt}\cos(\omega t+\phi_2)$ $\phi_1=\tan^{-1}\left[\dfrac{-b(b^2+3\omega^2)}{2\omega^3}\right],\ \phi_2=\tan^{-1}\left[\dfrac{\omega(3b^2-\omega^2)}{b(3\omega^2-b^2)}\right]$
376	$\dfrac{s^3}{(s+c)\left[(s+b)^2+\omega^2\right]^2}$	$-\dfrac{c^3}{\left[(b-c)^2+\omega^2\right]^2}\epsilon^{-ct}-\dfrac{1}{2\omega^2}\sqrt{\dfrac{b^2(3\omega^2-b^2)^2+\omega^2(3b^2-\omega^2)^2}{(c-b)^2+\omega^2}}\,t\epsilon^{-bt}\cos(\omega t+\phi_1)$ $+\dfrac{1}{2\omega^3\left[(c-b)^2+\omega^2\right]}\sqrt{4\omega^2\left[\omega^2(c-b)-b^3\right]^2+\left[\omega^2(\omega^2+3bc)+b^3(c-b)\right]^2}\,\epsilon^{-bt}\cos(\omega t+\phi_2)$ $\phi_1=\tan^{-1}\left[\dfrac{\omega(3b^2-\omega^2)}{b(3\omega^2-b^2)}\right]-\tan^{-1}\left(\dfrac{\omega}{c-b}\right),\ \phi_2=\tan^{-1}\left[\dfrac{\omega^2(\omega^2+3bc)+b^3(c-b)}{2\omega\left[\omega^2(c-b)-b^3\right]}\right]-2\tan^{-1}\left(\dfrac{\omega}{c-b}\right)$
377	$\dfrac{s^3}{\left[(s+b)^2+\omega^2\right]\left[(s+c)^2+d^2\right]}$	$\dfrac{1}{\omega}\sqrt{\dfrac{b^2(3\omega^2-b^2)^2+\omega^2(3b^2-\omega^2)^2}{\left[(c-b)^2+\omega^2-d^2\right]^2+4d^2(c-b)^2}}\,\epsilon^{-bt}\cos(\omega t-\phi_1)$ $+\dfrac{1}{d}\sqrt{\dfrac{c^2(3d^2-c^2)^2+d^2(3c^2-d^2)^2}{\left[(c-b)^2+\omega^2-d^2\right]^2+4d^2(c-b)^2}}\,\epsilon^{-ct}\cos(dt-\phi_2)$ $\phi_1=\tan^{-1}\left[\dfrac{b(3\omega^2-b^2)}{\omega(3b^2-\omega^2)}\right]+\tan^{-1}\left[\dfrac{2\omega(c-b)}{(c-b)^2-\omega^2+d^2}\right]$ $\phi_2=\tan^{-1}\left[\dfrac{c(3d^2-c^2)}{d(3c^2-d^2)}\right]+\tan^{-1}\left[\dfrac{2d(b-c)}{(c-b)^2-d^2+\omega^2}\right]$
378	$\dfrac{s^3}{(s+f)\left[(s+b)^2+\omega^2\right]\left[(s+c)^2+d^2\right]}$	$\dfrac{1}{\omega}\sqrt{\dfrac{b^2(3\omega^2-b^2)^2+\omega^2(3b^2-\omega^2)^2}{\left[(f-b)^2+\omega^2\right]\left\{\left[(c-b)^2+\omega^2-d^2\right]^2+4d^2(c-b)^2\right\}}}\,\epsilon^{-bt}\cos(\omega t-\phi_1)$ $+\dfrac{1}{d}\sqrt{\dfrac{c^2(3d^2-c^2)^2+d^2(3c^2-d^2)^2}{\left[(f-c)^2+d^2\right]\left\{\left[(c-b)^2+\omega^2-d^2\right]^2+4d^2(c-b)^2\right\}}}\,\epsilon^{-ct}\cos(dt-\phi_2)$ $-\dfrac{f^3}{\left[(b-f)^2+\omega^2\right]\left[(c-f)^2+d^2\right]}\epsilon^{-ft}$ $\phi_1=\tan^{-1}\left[\dfrac{b(3\omega^2-b^2)}{\omega(3b^2-\omega^2)}\right]+\tan^{-1}\left(\dfrac{\omega}{f-b}\right)+\tan^{-1}\left[\dfrac{2\omega(c-b)}{(c-b)^2-\omega^2+d^2}\right]$ $\phi_2=\tan^{-1}\left[\dfrac{c(3d^2-c^2)}{d(3c^2-d^2)}\right]+\tan^{-1}\left(\dfrac{d}{f-c}\right)+\tan^{-1}\left[\dfrac{2d(b-c)}{(c-b)^2+\omega^2-d^2}\right]$

NO.	F(s)	f(t)
379	$\frac{s^3}{s^4+4\omega^4}$	$\cos(\omega t)\cosh(\omega t)$
380	$\frac{s^3}{s^4-\omega^4}$	$\frac{1}{2}\left[\cosh(\omega t)+\cos(\omega t)\right]$
381	$\frac{s^3+a_2s^2+a_1s+a_0}{s^2(s+b)(s+c)}$	$\frac{a_0}{bc}t-\frac{a_0(b+c)-a_1bc}{b^2c^2}+\frac{-b^3+a_2b^2-a_1b+a_0}{b^2(c-b)}\epsilon^{-bt}+\frac{-c^3+a_2c^2-a_1c+a_0}{c^2(b-c)}\epsilon^{-ct}$
382	$\frac{s^3+a_2s^2+a_1s+a_0}{s(s+b)(s+c)(s+d)}$	$\frac{a_0}{bcd}-\frac{-b^3+a_2b^2-a_1b+a_0}{b(c-b)(d-b)}\epsilon^{-bt}-\frac{-c^3+a_2c^2-a_1c+a_0}{c(b-c)(d-c)}\epsilon^{-ct}-\frac{-d^3+a_2d^2-a_1d+a_0}{d(b-d)(c-d)}\epsilon^{-dt}$
383	$\frac{s^3+a_2s^2+a_1s+a_0}{s^2(s+b)(s+c)(s+d)}$	$\frac{a_0}{bcd}t+\left[\frac{a_1}{bcd}-\frac{a_0(bc+bd+cd)}{b^2c^2d^2}\right]+\frac{-b^3+a_2b^2-a_1b+a_0}{b^2(c-b)(d-b)}\epsilon^{-bt}$ $+\frac{-c^3+a_2c^2-a_1c+a_0}{c^2(b-c)(d-c)}\epsilon^{-ct}+\frac{-d^3+a_2d^2-a_1d+a_0}{d^2(b-d)(c-d)}\epsilon^{-dt}$
384	$\frac{s^3+a_2s^2+a_1s+a_0}{(s+b)(s+c)(s+d)(s+f)}$	$\frac{-b^3+a_2b^2-a_1b+a_0}{(c-b)(d-b)(f-b)}\epsilon^{-bt}+\frac{-c^3+a_2c^2-a_1c+a_0}{(b-c)(d-c)(f-c)}\epsilon^{-ct}+\frac{-d^3+a_2d^2-a_1d+a_0}{(b-d)(c-d)(f-d)}\epsilon^{-dt}$ $+\frac{-f^3+a_2f^2-a_1f+a_0}{(b-f)(c-f)(d-f)}\epsilon^{-ft}$
385	$\frac{s^3+a_2s^2+a_1s+a_0}{s(s+b)(s+c)(s+d)(s+f)}$	$\frac{a_0}{bcdf}-\frac{-b^3+a_2b^2-a_1b+a_0}{b(c-b)(d-b)(f-b)}\epsilon^{-bt}-\frac{-c^3+a_2c^2-a_1c+a_0}{c(b-c)(d-c)(f-c)}\epsilon^{-ct}$ $-\frac{-d^3+a_2d^2-a_1d+a_0}{d(b-d)(c-d)(f-d)}\epsilon^{-dt}-\frac{-f^3+a_2f^2-a_1f+a_0}{f(b-f)(c-f)(d-f)}\epsilon^{-ft}$
386	$\frac{s^3+a_2s^2+a_1s+a_0}{(s+b)(s+c)(s+d)(s+f)(s+g)}$	$\frac{-b^3+a_2b^2-a_1b+a_0}{(c-b)(d-b)(f-b)(g-b)}\epsilon^{-bt}+\frac{-c^3+a_2c^2-a_1c+a_0}{(b-c)(d-c)(f-c)(g-c)}\epsilon^{-ct}+\frac{-d^3+a_2d^2-a_1d+a_0}{(b-d)(c-d)(f-d)(g-d)}\epsilon^{-dt}$ $+\frac{-f^3+a_2f^2-a_1f+a_0}{(b-f)(c-f)(d-f)(g-f)}\epsilon^{-ft}+\frac{-g^3+a_2g^2-a_1g+a_0}{(b-g)(c-g)(d-g)(f-g)}\epsilon^{-gt}$
387	$\frac{s^3+a_2s^2+a_1s+a_0}{(s+b)(s+c)(s+d)^2}$	$\frac{-b^3+a_2b^2-a_1b+a_0}{(c-b)(d-b)^2}\epsilon^{-bt}+\frac{-c^3+a_2c^2-a_1c+a_0}{(b-c)(d-c)^2}\epsilon^{-ct}+\frac{-d^3+a_2d^2-a_1d+a_0}{(b-d)(c-d)}t\epsilon^{-dt}$ $+\frac{a_0(2d-b-c)+a_1(bc-d^2)+a_2d(db+dc-2bc)+d^2(d^2-2db-2dc+3bc)}{(b-d)^2(c-d)^2}\epsilon^{-dt}$
388	$\frac{s^3+a_2s^2+a_1s+a_0}{s(s+b)(s+c)(s+d)^2}$	$\frac{a_0}{bcd^2}-\frac{-b^3+a_2b^2-a_1b+a_0}{b(c-b)(d-b)^2}\epsilon^{-bt}-\frac{-c^3+a_2c^2-a_1c+a_0}{c(b-c)(d-c)^2}\epsilon^{-ct}-\frac{-d^3+a_2d^2-a_1d+a_0}{d(b-d)(c-d)}t\epsilon^{-dt}$ $-\frac{3d^2-2a_2d+a_1}{d(b-d)(c-d)}\epsilon^{-dt}-\frac{(-d^3+a_2d^2-a_1d+a_0)[(b-d)(c-d)-d(b-d)-d(c-d)]}{d^2(b-d)^2(c-d)^2}\epsilon^{-dt}$
389	$\frac{s^3+a_2s^2+a_1s+a_0}{(s+b)(s+c)(s+d)(s+f)^2}$	$\frac{-b^3+a_2b^2-a_1b+a_0}{(c-b)(d-b)(f-b)^2}\epsilon^{-bt}+\frac{-c^3+a_2c^2-a_1c+a_0}{(b-c)(d-c)(f-c)^2}\epsilon^{-ct}+\frac{-d^3+a_2d^2-a_1d+a_0}{(b-d)(c-d)(f-d)^2}\epsilon^{-dt}$ $+\frac{-f^3+a_2f^2-a_1f+a_0}{(b-f)(c-f)(d-f)}t\epsilon^{-ft}+\frac{3f^2-2a_2f+a_1}{(b-f)(c-f)(d-f)}\epsilon^{-ft}$ $-\frac{(-f^3+a_2f^2-a_1f+a_0)[(b-f)(c-f)+(b-f)(d-f)+(c-f)(d-f)]}{(b-f)^2(c-f)^2(d-f)^2}\epsilon^{-ft}$

NO.	F(s)	f(t)
390	$\frac{s^3+a_2s^2+a_1s+a_0}{s^2(s+b)^2}$	$\frac{a_0}{b^2}t-\frac{2a_0-a_1b}{b^3}+\frac{1}{b^2}\left[(-b^3+a_2b^2-a_1b+a_0)t+\frac{2a_0-a_1b+b^3}{b}\right]\epsilon^{-bt}$
391	$\frac{s^3+a_2s^2+a_1s+a_0}{s(s+b)(s+c)^2}$	$\frac{a_0}{bc^2}-\frac{-b^3+a_2b^2-a_1b+a_0}{b(c-b)^2}\epsilon^{-bt}-\frac{-c^3+a_2c^2-a_1c+a_0}{c(b-c)}t\epsilon^{-ct}-\frac{a_0(b-2c)+a_1c^2-a_2bc^2+c^3(2b-c)}{c^2(b-c)^2}\epsilon^{-ct}$
392	$\frac{s^3+a_2s^2+a_1s+a_0}{s^2(s+b)(s+c)^2}$	$\frac{a_0}{bc^2}t+\left[\frac{a_1}{bc^2}-\frac{a_0(2b+c)}{b^3c^3}\right]+\frac{-c^3+a_2c^2-a_1c+a_0}{c^2(b-c)}t\epsilon^{-ct}+\left[\frac{3c^2-2a_2c+a_1}{c^2(b-c)}+\frac{(-c^3+a_2c^2-a_1c+a_0)(2b-3c)}{c^3(b-c)^2}\right]\epsilon^{-ct}+\frac{-b^3+a_2b^2-a_1b+a_0}{b^2(c-b)^2}\epsilon^{-bt}$
393	$\frac{s^3+a_2s^2+a_1s+a_0}{(s+b)^2(s+c)^2}$	$\frac{-b^3+a_2b^2-a_1b+a_0}{(c-b)^2}t\epsilon^{-bt}-\frac{2a_0-a_1(b+c)+2a_2bc-b^2(3c-b)}{(c-b)^3}\epsilon^{-bt}+\frac{-c^3+a_2c^2-a_1c+a_0}{(b-c)^2}t\epsilon^{-ct}-\frac{2a_0-a_1(b+c)+2a_2bc-c^2(3b-c)}{(b-c)^3}\epsilon^{-ct}$
394	$\frac{s^3+a_2s^2+a_1s+a_0}{s(s+b)^2(s+c)^2}$	$\frac{a_0}{b^2c^2}-\frac{-b^3+a_2b^2-a_1b+a_0}{b(c-b)^2}t\epsilon^{-bt}-\left[\frac{3b^2-2a_2b+a_1}{b(c-b)^2}+\frac{(-b^3+a_2b^2-a_1b+a_0)(c-3b)}{b^2(c-b)^3}\right]\epsilon^{-bt}-\frac{-c^3+a_2c^2-a_1c+a_0}{c(b-c)^2}t\epsilon^{-ct}-\left[\frac{3c^2-2a_2c+a_1}{c(b-c)^2}+\frac{(-c^3+a_2c^2-a_1c+a_0)(b-3c)}{c^2(b-c)^3}\right]\epsilon^{-ct}$
395	$\frac{s^3+a_2s^2+a_1s+a_0}{(s+d)(s+b)^2(s+c)^2}$	$\frac{-b^3+a_2b^2-a_1b+a_0}{(c-b)^2(d-b)}t\epsilon^{-bt}+\left[\frac{3b^2-2a_2b+a_1}{(c-b)^2(d-b)}-\frac{(-b^3+a_2b^2-a_1b+a_0)(c+2d-3b)}{(c-b)^3(d-b)^2}\right]\epsilon^{-bt}+\frac{-c^3+a_2c^2-a_1c+a_0}{(b-c)^2(d-c)}t\epsilon^{-ct}+\left[\frac{3c^2-2a_2c+a_1}{(b-c)^2(d-c)}-\frac{(-c^3+a_2c^2-a_1c+a_0)(b+2d-3c)}{(b-c)^3(d-c)^2}\right]\epsilon^{-ct}+\frac{-d^3+a_2d^2-a_1d+a_0}{(b-d)^2(c-d)}\epsilon^{-dt}$
396	$\frac{s^3+a_2s^2+a_1s+a_0}{s^2(s^2+\omega^2)}$	$\frac{a_0}{\omega^2}t+\frac{a_1}{\omega^2}-\frac{1}{\omega^3}\sqrt{(a_0-a_2\omega^2)^2+\omega^2(a_1-\omega^2)^2}\cos(\omega t-\phi);\ \phi=\tan^{-1}\left[\frac{a_0-a_2\omega^2}{\omega(a_1-\omega^2)}\right]$
397	$\frac{s^3+a_2s^2+a_1s+a_0}{s(s+b)(s^2+\omega^2)}$	$\frac{a_0}{b\omega^2}-\frac{-b^3+a_2b^2-a_1b+a_0}{b(b^2+\omega^2)}\epsilon^{-bt}-\frac{1}{\omega^2}\sqrt{\frac{(a_0-a_2\omega^2)^2+\omega^2(a_1-\omega^2)^2}{b^2+\omega^2}}\cos(\omega t+\phi)$ $\phi=\tan^{-1}\left[\frac{\omega(a_1-\omega^2)}{a_0-a_2\omega^2}\right]-\tan^{-1}\left(\frac{\omega}{b}\right)$
398	$\frac{s^3+a_2s^2+a_1s+a_0}{s^2(s+b)(s^2+\omega^2)}$	$\frac{a_0}{b\omega^2}t+\left[\frac{a_1}{b\omega^2}-\frac{a_0}{b^2\omega^2}\right]+\frac{-b^3+a_2b^2-a_1b+a_0}{b^2(b^2+\omega^2)}\epsilon^{-bt}-\frac{1}{\omega^3}\sqrt{\frac{(a_0-a_2\omega^2)^2+\omega^2(a_1-\omega^2)^2}{b^2+\omega^2}}\cos(\omega t-\phi)$ $\phi=\tan^{-1}\left[\frac{a_0-a_2\omega^2}{\omega(a_1-\omega^2)}\right]+\tan^{-1}\left(\frac{\omega}{b}\right)$

NO.	F(s)	f(t)
399	$\dfrac{s^3+a_2s^2+a_1s+a_0}{(s+b)(s+c)(s^2+\omega^2)}$	$\dfrac{-b^3+a_2b^2-a_1b+a_0}{(c-b)(b^2+\omega^2)}\epsilon^{-bt}+\dfrac{-c^3+a_2c^2-a_1c+a_0}{(b-c)(c^2+\omega^2)}\epsilon^{-ct}$ $+\dfrac{1}{\omega}\sqrt{\dfrac{(a_0-a_2\omega^2)^2+\omega^2(a_1-\omega^2)^2}{(b^2+\omega^2)(c^2+\omega^2)}}\sin(\omega t+\phi)$ $\phi=\tan^{-1}\left[\dfrac{\omega(a_1-\omega^2)}{a_0-a_2\omega^2}\right]-\tan^{-1}\left(\dfrac{\omega}{b}\right)-\tan^{-1}\left(\dfrac{\omega}{c}\right)$
400	$\dfrac{s^3+a_2s^2+a_1s+a_0}{s(s+b)(s+c)(s^2+\omega^2)}$	$\dfrac{a_0}{bc\omega^2}-\dfrac{-b^3+a_2b^2-a_1b+a_0}{b(c-b)(b^2+\omega^2)}\epsilon^{-bt}-\dfrac{-c^3+a_2c^2-a_1c+a_0}{c(b-c)(c^2+\omega^2)}\epsilon^{-ct}$ $-\dfrac{1}{\omega^2}\sqrt{\dfrac{(a_0-a_2\omega^2)^2+\omega^2(a_1-\omega^2)^2}{(b^2+\omega^2)(c^2+\omega^2)}}\cos(\omega t+\phi)$ $\phi=\tan^{-1}\left[\dfrac{\omega(a_1-\omega^2)}{a_0-a_2\omega^2}\right]-\tan^{-1}\left(\dfrac{\omega}{b}\right)-\tan^{-1}\left(\dfrac{\omega}{c}\right)$
401	$\dfrac{s^3+a_2s^2+a_1s+a_0}{(s+b)(s+c)(s+d)(s^2+\omega^2)}$	$\dfrac{-b^3+a_2b^2-a_1b+a_0}{(c-b)(d-b)(b^2+\omega^2)}\epsilon^{-bt}+\dfrac{-c^3+a_2c^2-a_1c+a_0}{(b-c)(d-c)(c^2+\omega^2)}\epsilon^{-ct}+\dfrac{-d^3+a_2d^2-a_1d+a_0}{(b-d)(c-d)(d^2+\omega^2)}\epsilon^{-dt}$ $+\dfrac{1}{\omega}\sqrt{\dfrac{(a_0-a_2\omega^2)^2+\omega^2(a_1-\omega^2)^2}{(b^2+\omega^2)(c^2+\omega^2)(d^2+\omega^2)}}\cos(\omega t-\phi)$ $\phi=\tan^{-1}\left[\dfrac{a_0-a_2\omega^2}{\omega(a_1-\omega^2)}\right]+\tan^{-1}\left(\dfrac{\omega}{b}\right)+\tan^{-1}\left(\dfrac{\omega}{c}\right)+\tan^{-1}\left(\dfrac{\omega}{d}\right)$
402	$\dfrac{s^3+a_2s^2+a_1s+a_0}{(s+b)^2(s^2+\omega^2)}$	$\dfrac{-b^3+a_2b^2-a_1b+a_0}{b^2+\omega^2}t\epsilon^{-bt}+\dfrac{2a_0b+a_1(\omega^2-b^2)-2a_2b\omega^2+b^2(b^2+3\omega^2)}{(b^2+\omega^2)^2}\epsilon^{-bt}$ $-\dfrac{1}{\omega(b^2+\omega^2)}\sqrt{(a_0-a_2\omega^2)^2+\omega^2(a_1-\omega^2)^2}\cos(\omega t+\phi)$ $\phi=\tan^{-1}\left[\dfrac{\omega(a_1-\omega^2)}{a_0-a_2\omega^2}\right]+\tan^{-1}\left(\dfrac{b}{\omega}\right)-\tan^{-1}\left(\dfrac{\omega}{b}\right)$
403	$\dfrac{s^3+a_2s^2+a_1s+a_0}{s(s+b)^2(s^2+\omega^2)}$	$\dfrac{a_0}{b^2\omega^2}-\dfrac{-b^3+a_2b^2-a_1b+a_0}{b(b^2+\omega^2)}t\epsilon^{-bt}-\left[\dfrac{3b^2-2a_2b+a_1}{b(b^2+\omega^2)}+\dfrac{(-b^3+a_2b^2-a_1b+a_0)(\omega^2+3b^2)}{b^2(b^2+\omega^2)^2}\right]\epsilon^{-bt}$ $-\dfrac{1}{\omega^2(b^2+\omega^2)}\sqrt{(a_0-a_2\omega^2)^2+\omega^2(a_1-\omega^2)^2}\cos(\omega t+\phi)$ $\phi=\tan^{-1}\left[\dfrac{\omega(a_1-\omega^2)}{a_0-a_2\omega^2}\right]-2\tan^{-1}\left(\dfrac{\omega}{b}\right)$
404	$\dfrac{s^3+a_2s^2+a_1s+a_0}{(s+c)(s+b)^2(s^2+\omega^2)}$	$\dfrac{-c^3+a_2c^2-a_1c+a_0}{(b-c)^2(c^2+\omega^2)}\epsilon^{-ct}+\dfrac{1}{\omega(b^2+\omega^2)}\sqrt{\dfrac{(a_0-a_2\omega^2)^2+\omega^2(a_1-\omega^2)^2}{c^2+\omega^2}}\cos(\omega t-\phi)$ $+\dfrac{-b^3+a_2b^2-a_1b+a_0}{(c-b)(b^2+\omega^2)}t\epsilon^{-bt}+\left[\dfrac{3b^2-2a_2b+a_1}{(c-b)(b^2+\omega^2)}\right.$ $\left.-\dfrac{(-b^3+a_2b^2-a_1b+a_0)(\omega^2+3b^2-2bc)}{(c-b)^2(b^2+\omega^2)^2}\right]\epsilon^{-bt}$ $\phi=\tan^{-1}\left[\dfrac{a_0-a_2\omega^2}{\omega(a_1-\omega^2)}\right]+\tan^{-1}\left(\dfrac{\omega}{c}\right)+2\tan^{-1}\left(\dfrac{\omega}{b}\right)$

NO.	F(s)	f(t)
405	$\frac{s^3+a_2s^2+a_1s+a_0}{(s^2+b^2)(s^2+\omega^2)}$	$\frac{1}{b(\omega^2-b^2)}\sqrt{(a_0-a_2b^2)^2+b^2(a_1-b^2)^2}\ \sin(bt+\phi_1)$ $+\frac{1}{\omega(b^2-\omega^2)}\sqrt{(a_0-a_2\omega^2)^2+\omega^2(a_1-\omega^2)^2}\ \sin(\omega t+\phi_2)$ $\phi_1=\tan^{-1}\left[\frac{b(a_1-b^2)}{a_0-a_2b^2}\right]$, $\phi_2=\tan^{-1}\left[\frac{\omega(a_1-\omega^2)}{a_0-a_2\omega^2}\right]$
406	$\frac{s^3+a_2s^2+a_1s+a_0}{s(s^2+b^2)(s^2+\omega^2)}$	$\frac{a_0}{b^2\omega^2}-\frac{1}{b^2(\omega^2-b^2)}\sqrt{(a_0-a_2b^2)^2+b^2(a_1-b^2)^2}\ \cos(bt+\phi_1)$ $-\frac{1}{\omega^2(b^2-\omega^2)}\sqrt{(a_0-a_2\omega^2)^2+\omega^2(a_1-\omega^2)^2}\ \cos(\omega t+\phi_2)$ $\phi_1=\tan^{-1}\left[\frac{b(a_1-b^2)}{a_0-a_2b^2}\right]$, $\phi_2=\tan^{-1}\left[\frac{\omega(a_1-\omega^2)}{a_0-a_2\omega^2}\right]$
407	$\frac{s^3+a_2s^2+a_1s+a_0}{(s+c)(s^2+b^2)(s^2+\omega^2)}$	$\frac{-c^3+a_2c^2-a_1c+a_0}{(c^2+b^2)(c^2+\omega^2)}\epsilon^{-ct}+\frac{1}{b(\omega^2-b^2)}\sqrt{\frac{(a_0-a_2b^2)^2+b^2(a_1-b^2)^2}{c^2+b^2}}\ \cos(bt-\phi_1)$ $+\frac{1}{\omega(b^2-\omega^2)}\sqrt{\frac{(a_0-a_2\omega^2)^2+\omega^2(a_1-\omega^2)^2}{c^2+\omega^2}}\ \cos(\omega t-\phi_2)$ $\phi_1=\tan^{-1}\left[\frac{a_0-a_2b^2}{b(a_1-b^2)}\right]+\tan^{-1}\left(\frac{b}{c}\right)$, $\phi_2=\tan^{-1}\left[\frac{a_0-a_2\omega^2}{\omega(a_1-\omega^2)}\right]+\tan^{-1}\left(\frac{\omega}{c}\right)$
408	$\frac{s^3+a_2s^2+a_1s+a_0}{(s^2+\omega^2)^2}$	$\frac{1}{2\omega^3}\sqrt{4\omega^6+(a_0+a_2\omega^2)^2}\ \cos(\omega t-\phi_1)-\frac{1}{2\omega^2}\sqrt{(a_0-a_2\omega^2)^2+\omega^2(a_1-\omega^2)^2}\ t\cos(\omega t+\phi_2)$ $\phi_1=\tan^{-1}\left[\frac{a_0+a_2\omega^2}{2\omega^3}\right]$, $\phi_2=\tan^{-1}\left[\frac{\omega(a_1-\omega^2)}{a_0-a_2\omega^2}\right]$
409	$\frac{s^3+a_2s^2+a_1s+a_0}{s(s^2+\omega^2)^2}$	$\frac{a_0}{\omega^4}-\frac{1}{2\omega^3}\sqrt{(a_0-a_2\omega^2)^2+\omega^2(a_1-\omega^2)^2}\ t\cos(\omega t-\phi_1)$ $-\frac{1}{2\omega^4}\sqrt{4a_0^2+\omega^2(a_1+\omega^2)^2}\ \cos(\omega t+\phi_2)$ $\phi_1=\tan^{-1}\left[\frac{a_0-a_2\omega^2}{\omega(a_1-\omega^2)}\right]$ $\phi_2=\tan^{-1}\left[\frac{\omega(a_1+\omega^2)}{2a_0}\right]$
410	$\frac{s^3+a_2s^2+a_1s+a_0}{s^2(s^2+\omega^2)^2}$	$\frac{a_0}{\omega^4}t+\frac{a_1}{\omega^4}-\frac{1}{2\omega^5}\sqrt{4a_1^2\omega^2+(3a_0-a_2\omega^2)^2}\ \sin(\omega t+\phi_1)$ $+\frac{1}{2\omega^4}\sqrt{(a_0-a_2\omega^2)^2+\omega^2(a_1-\omega^2)^2}\ t\cos(\omega t+\phi_2)$ $\phi_1=\tan^{-1}\left[\frac{2a_1\omega}{3a_0-a_2\omega^2}\right]$ $\phi_2=\tan^{-1}\left[\frac{\omega(a_1-\omega^2)}{a_0-a_2\omega^2}\right]$

NO.	F(s)	f(t)
411	$\dfrac{s^3+a_2s^2+a_1s+a_0}{(s+b)(s^2+\omega^2)^2}$	$\dfrac{-b^3+a_2b^2-a_1b+a_0}{(b^2+\omega^2)^2}\epsilon^{-bt}-\dfrac{1}{2\omega^2}\sqrt{\dfrac{(a_0-a_2\omega^2)^2+\omega^2(a_1-\omega^2)^2}{b^2+\omega^2}}\,t\cos(\omega t+\phi_1)$ $+\dfrac{1}{2\omega^3(b^2+\omega^2)}\sqrt{4\omega^2(a_0+b\omega^2)^2+[\omega^2(a_1-a_2b+\omega^2)-ba_0]^2}\cos(\omega t+\phi_2)$ $\phi_1=\tan^{-1}\left[\dfrac{\omega(a_1-\omega^2)}{a_0-a_2\omega^2}\right]-\tan^{-1}\left(\dfrac{\omega}{b}\right)$ $\phi_2=\tan^{-1}\left[\dfrac{\omega^2(a_1-a_2b+\omega^2)-a_0b}{2\omega(a_0+b\omega^2)}\right]-2\tan^{-1}\left(\dfrac{\omega}{b}\right)$
412	$\dfrac{s^3+a_2s^2+a_1s+a_0}{s^2[(s+b)^2+\omega^2]}$	$\dfrac{a_0}{b^2+\omega^2}t-\dfrac{2a_0b-a_1(b^2+\omega^2)}{(b^2+\omega^2)^2}+\dfrac{1}{\omega(b^2+\omega^2)}\sqrt{R^2+Q^2}\,\epsilon^{-bt}\cos(\omega t+\phi)$ $R=[b(3\omega^2-b^2)+a_2(b^2-\omega^2)-a_1b+a_0],\ Q=\omega[3b^2-\omega^2-2a_2b+a_1]$ $\phi=\tan^{-1}\left(\dfrac{Q}{R}\right)-\tan^{-1}\left(\dfrac{b}{\omega}\right)+\tan^{-1}\left(\dfrac{\omega}{b}\right)$
413	$\dfrac{s^3+a_2s^2+a_1s+a_0}{s(s+c)[(s+b)^2+\omega^2]}$	$\dfrac{a_0}{c(b^2+\omega^2)}-\dfrac{-c^3+a_2c^2-a_1c+a_0}{c[(b-c)^2+\omega^2]}\epsilon^{-ct}-\dfrac{1}{\omega}\sqrt{\dfrac{R^2+Q^2}{(b^2+\omega^2)[(c-b)^2+\omega^2]}}\,\epsilon^{-bt}\cos(\omega t+\phi)$ $R=[b(3\omega^2-b^2)+a_2(b^2-\omega^2)-a_1b+a_0],\ Q=\omega[3b^2-\omega^2-2a_2b+a_1]$ $\phi=\tan^{-1}\left(\dfrac{Q}{R}\right)-\tan^{-1}\left(\dfrac{b}{\omega}\right)-\tan^{-1}\left(\dfrac{\omega}{c-b}\right)$
414	$\dfrac{s^3+a_2s^2+a_1s+a_0}{s^2(s+c)[(s+b)^2+\omega^2]}$	$\dfrac{a_0}{c(b^2+\omega^2)}t+\left[\dfrac{a_1}{c(b^2+\omega^2)}-\dfrac{a_0(2bc+b^2+\omega^2)}{c^2(b^2+\omega^2)^2}\right]+\dfrac{-c^3+a_2c^2-a_1c+a_0}{c^2[(b-c)^2+\omega^2]}\epsilon^{-ct}$ $+\dfrac{1}{\omega(b^2+\omega^2)}\sqrt{\dfrac{R^2+Q^2}{(b-c)^2+\omega^2}}\,\epsilon^{-bt}\cos(\omega t-\phi)$ $R=[b(3\omega^2-b^2)+a_2(b^2-\omega^2)-a_1b+a_0],\ Q=\omega[3b^2-\omega^2-2a_2b+a_1]$ $\phi=\tan^{-1}\left(\dfrac{R}{Q}\right)+\tan^{-1}\left(\dfrac{\omega}{c-b}\right)-2\tan^{-1}\left(\dfrac{\omega}{b}\right)$
415	$\dfrac{s^3+a_2s^2+a_1s+a_0}{(s+c)(s+d)[(s+b)^2+\omega^2]}$	$\dfrac{-c^3+a_2c^2-a_1c+a_0}{(d-c)[(b-c)^2+\omega^2]}\epsilon^{-ct}+\dfrac{-d^3+a_2d^2-a_1d+a_0}{(c-d)[(b-d)^2+\omega^2]}\epsilon^{-dt}$ $+\dfrac{1}{\omega}\sqrt{\dfrac{R^2+Q^2}{[(d-b)^2+\omega^2][(c-b)^2+\omega^2]}}\,\epsilon^{-bt}\cos(\omega t-\phi)$ $R=[b(3\omega^2-b^2)+a_2(b^2-\omega^2)-a_1b+a_0],\ Q=\omega[3b^2-\omega^2-2a_2b+a_1]$ $\phi=\tan^{-1}\left(\dfrac{R}{Q}\right)+\tan^{-1}\left(\dfrac{\omega}{c-b}\right)+\tan^{-1}\left(\dfrac{\omega}{d-b}\right)$

NO.	F(s)	f(t)
416	$\dfrac{s^3+a_2s^2+a_1s+a_0}{s(s+c)(s+d)[(s+b)^2+\omega^2]}$	$\dfrac{a_0}{cd(b^2+\omega^2)} - \dfrac{-c^3+a_2c^2-a_1c+a_0}{c(d-c)[(b-c)^2+\omega^2]}\epsilon^{-ct} - \dfrac{-d^3+a_2d^2-a_1d+a_0}{d(c-d)[(b-d)^2+\omega^2]}\epsilon^{-dt}$ $-\dfrac{1}{\omega}\sqrt{\dfrac{R^2+Q^2}{(b^2+\omega^2)[(c-b)^2+\omega^2][(d-b)^2+\omega^2]}}\,\epsilon^{-bt}\cos(\omega t+\phi)$ $R=[b(3\omega^2-b^2)+a_2(b^2-\omega^2)-a_1b+a_0]$, $Q=\omega[3b^2-\omega^2-2a_2b+a_1]$ $\phi=\tan^{-1}\left(\dfrac{Q}{R}\right)-\tan^{-1}\left(\dfrac{b}{\omega}\right)-\tan^{-1}\left(\dfrac{\omega}{c-b}\right)-\tan^{-1}\left(\dfrac{\omega}{d-b}\right)$
417	$\dfrac{s^3+a_2s^2+a_1s+a_0}{(s+c)^2[(s+b)^2+\omega^2]}$	$\dfrac{1}{\omega[(c-b)^2+\omega^2]}\sqrt{R^2+Q^2}\,\epsilon^{-bt}\cos(\omega t-\phi)+\dfrac{-c^3+a_2c^2-a_1c+a_0}{[(b-c)^2+\omega^2]}t\epsilon^{-ct}$ $+\dfrac{c^2(c^2-4bc+3b^2+3\omega^2)-2a_2c(b^2+\omega^2-bc)+a_1(b^2+\omega^2-c^2)+2a_0(c-b)}{[(b-c)^2+\omega^2]^2}\epsilon^{-ct}$ $R=[b(3\omega^2-b^2)+a_2(b^2-\omega^2)-a_1b+a_0]$, $Q=\omega[3b^2-\omega^2-2a_2b+a_1]$ $\phi=\tan^{-1}\left(\dfrac{R}{Q}\right)+2\tan^{-1}\left(\dfrac{\omega}{c-b}\right)$
418	$\dfrac{s^3+a_2s^2+a_1s+a_0}{s(s+c)^2[(s+b)^2+\omega^2]}$	$\dfrac{a_0}{c^2(b^2+\omega^2)}-\dfrac{1}{\omega[(c-b)^2+\omega^2]}\sqrt{\dfrac{R^2+Q^2}{b^2+\omega^2}}\,\epsilon^{-bt}\cos(\omega t+\phi)-\dfrac{-c^3+a_2c^2-a_1c+a_0}{c[(b-c)^2+\omega^2]}t\epsilon^{-ct}$ $-\left[\dfrac{3c^2-2a_2c+a_1}{c[(b-c)^2+\omega^2]}+\dfrac{(-c^3+a_2c^2-a_1c+a_0)[(b-c)^2+\omega^2-2c(b-c)]}{c^2[(b-c)^2+\omega^2]^2}\right]\epsilon^{-ct}$ $R=[b(3\omega^2-b^2)+a_2(b^2-\omega^2)-a_1b+a_0]$, $Q=\omega[3b^2-\omega^2-2a_2b+a_1]$ $\phi=\tan^{-1}\left(\dfrac{Q}{R}\right)-\tan^{-1}\left(\dfrac{b}{\omega}\right)-2\tan^{-1}\left(\dfrac{\omega}{c-b}\right)$
419	$\dfrac{s^3+a_2s^2+a_1s+a_0}{(s+c)(s+d)^2[(s+b)^2+\omega^2]}$	$\dfrac{-c^3+a_2c^2-a_1c+a_0}{(d-c)^2[(b-c)^2+\omega^2]}\epsilon^{-ct}+\dfrac{1}{\omega[(d-b)^2+\omega^2]}\sqrt{\dfrac{R^2+Q^2}{(c-b)^2+\omega^2}}\,\epsilon^{-bt}\cos(\omega t-\phi)$ $+\dfrac{-d^3+a_2d^2-a_1d+a_0}{(c-d)[(b-d)^2+\omega^2]}t\epsilon^{-dt}+\left[\dfrac{3d^2-2a_2d+a_1}{(c-d)[(b-d)^2+\omega^2]}\right.$ $\left.-\dfrac{(-d^3+a_2d^2-a_1d+a_0)[(b-d)^2+\omega^2+2(c-d)(b-d)]}{(c-d)^2[(b-d)^2+\omega^2]^2}\right]\epsilon^{-dt}$ $R=[b(3\omega^2-b^2)+a_2(b^2-\omega^2)-a_1b+a_0]$ $Q=\omega[3b^2-\omega^2-2a_2b+a_1]$ $\phi=\tan^{-1}\left(\dfrac{R}{Q}\right)+\tan^{-1}\left(\dfrac{\omega}{c-b}\right)+2\tan^{-1}\left(\dfrac{\omega}{d-b}\right)$

NO.	F(s)	f(t)
420	$\dfrac{s^3+a_2s^2+a_1s+a_o}{(s+c)(s+d)(s+f)\left[(s+b)^2+\omega^2\right]}$	$\dfrac{-c^3+a_2c^2-a_1c+a_o}{(d-c)(f-c)\left[(b-c)^2+\omega^2\right]}\epsilon^{-ct}+\dfrac{-d^3+a_2d^2-a_1d+a_o}{(c-d)(f-d)\left[(b-d)^2+\omega^2\right]}\epsilon^{-dt}+\dfrac{-f^3+a_2f^2-a_1f+a_o}{(c-f)(d-f)\left[(b-f)^2+\omega^2\right]}\epsilon^{-ft}$ $+\dfrac{1}{\omega}\sqrt{\dfrac{R^2+Q^2}{\left[(c-b)^2+\omega^2\right]\left[(d-b)^2+\omega^2\right]\left[(f-b)^2+\omega^2\right]}}\,\epsilon^{-bt}\cos(\omega t-\phi)$ $R=\left[b(3\omega^2-b^2)+a_2(b^2-\omega^2)-a_1b+a_o\right],\ Q=\omega\left[3b^2-\omega^2-2a_2b+a_1\right]$ $\phi=\tan^{-1}\left(\dfrac{R}{Q}\right)+\tan^{-1}\left(\dfrac{\omega}{c-b}\right)+\tan^{-1}\left(\dfrac{\omega}{d-b}\right)+\tan^{-1}\left(\dfrac{\omega}{f-b}\right)$
421	$\dfrac{s^3+a_2s^2+a_1s+a_o}{(s^2+c^2)\left[(s+b)^2+\omega^2\right]}$	$\dfrac{1}{c}\sqrt{\dfrac{(a_o-a_2c^2)^2+c^2(a_1-c^2)^2}{(b^2+\omega^2-c^2)^2+4b^2c^2}}\cos(ct-\phi_1)+\dfrac{1}{\omega}\sqrt{\dfrac{R^2+Q^2}{(b^2+\omega^2-c^2)^2+4b^2c^2}}\,\epsilon^{-bt}\cos(\omega t-\phi_2)$ $R=\left[b(3\omega^2-b^2)+a_2(b^2-\omega^2)-a_1b+a_o\right],\ Q=\omega\left[3b^2-\omega^2-2a_2b+a_1\right]$ $\phi_1=\tan^{-1}\left[\dfrac{a_o-a_2c^2}{c(a_1-c^2)}\right]+\tan^{-1}\left(\dfrac{2bc}{b^2+\omega^2-c^2}\right),\ \phi_2=\tan^{-1}\left(\dfrac{R}{Q}\right)-\tan^{-1}\left(\dfrac{2b\omega}{b^2-\omega^2+c^2}\right)$
422	$\dfrac{s^3+a_2s^2+a_1s+a_o}{s(s^2+c^2)\left[(s+b)^2+\omega^2\right]}$	$\dfrac{a_o}{c^2(b^2+\omega^2)}-\dfrac{1}{c^2}\sqrt{\dfrac{(a_o-a_2c^2)^2+c^2(a_1-c^2)^2}{(b^2+\omega^2-c^2)^2+4b^2c^2}}\cos(ct+\phi_1)$ $-\dfrac{1}{\omega}\sqrt{\dfrac{R^2+Q^2}{\left[(b^2+\omega^2-c^2)^2+4b^2c^2\right](b^2+\omega^2)}}\,\epsilon^{-bt}\cos(\omega t+\phi_2)$ $R=\left[b(3\omega^2-b^2)+a_2(b^2-\omega^2)-a_1b+a_o\right],\ Q=\omega\left[3b^2-\omega^2-2a_2b+a_1\right]$ $\phi_1=\tan^{-1}\left[\dfrac{c(a_1-c^2)}{a_o-a_2c^2}\right]-\tan^{-1}\left(\dfrac{2bc}{b^2+\omega^2-c^2}\right),\ \phi_2=\tan^{-1}\left(\dfrac{Q}{R}\right)-\tan^{-1}\left(\dfrac{b^2-\omega^2+c^2}{2b\omega}\right)+\tan^{-1}\left(\dfrac{\omega}{b}\right)$
423	$\dfrac{s^3+a_2s^2+a_1s+a_o}{(s+d)(s^2+c^2)\left[(s+b)^2+\omega^2\right]}$	$\dfrac{-d^3+a_2d^2-a_1d+a_o}{(d^2+c^2)\left[(b-d)^2+\omega^2\right]}\epsilon^{-dt}+\dfrac{1}{c}\sqrt{\dfrac{(a_o-a_2c^2)^2+c^2(a_1-c^2)^2}{(d^2+c^2)\left[(b^2+\omega^2-c^2)^2+4b^2c^2\right]}}\cos(ct-\phi_1)$ $+\dfrac{1}{\omega}\sqrt{\dfrac{R^2+Q^2}{\left[(d-b)^2+\omega^2\right]\left[(b^2+\omega^2-c^2)^2+4b^2c^2\right]}}\,\epsilon^{-bt}\cos(\omega t-\phi_2)$ $R=\left[b(3\omega^2-b^2)+a_2(b^2-\omega^2)-a_1b+a_o\right],\ Q=\omega\left[3b^2-\omega^2-2a_2b+a_1\right]$ $\phi_1=\tan^{-1}\left[\dfrac{a_o-a_2c^2}{c(a_1-c^2)}\right]+\tan^{-1}\left(\dfrac{c}{d}\right)+\tan^{-1}\left(\dfrac{2bc}{b^2+\omega^2-c^2}\right)$ $\phi_2=\tan^{-1}\left(\dfrac{R}{Q}\right)+\tan^{-1}\left(\dfrac{\omega}{d-b}\right)-\tan^{-1}\left(\dfrac{2b\omega}{b^2-\omega^2+c^2}\right)$
424	$\dfrac{s^3+a_2s^2+a_1s+a_o}{\left[(s+b)^2+\omega^2\right]^2}$	$\dfrac{1}{2\omega^3}\sqrt{4\omega^6+\left[a_o-a_1b+a_2(b^2+\omega^2)-b(b^2+3\omega^2)\right]^2}\,\epsilon^{-bt}\cos(\omega t-\phi_1)-\dfrac{1}{2\omega^2}\sqrt{R^2+Q^2}\,t\epsilon^{-bt}\cos(\omega t+\phi_2)$ $R=\left[b(3\omega^2-b^2)+a_2(b^2-\omega^2)-a_1b+a_o\right],\ Q=\omega\left[3b^2-\omega^2-2a_2b+a_1\right]$ $\phi_1=\tan^{-1}\left[\dfrac{a_o-a_1b+a_2(b^2+\omega^2)-b(b^2+3\omega^2)}{2\omega^3}\right],\ \phi_2=\tan^{-1}\left(\dfrac{Q}{R}\right)$

NO.	F(s)	f(t)
425	$\dfrac{s^3+a_2s^2+a_1s+a_0}{s\left[(s+b)^2+\omega^2\right]^2}$	$\dfrac{a_0}{(b^2+\omega^2)^2}-\dfrac{1}{2\omega^2}\sqrt{\dfrac{R^2+Q^2}{b^2+\omega^2}}\;t\epsilon^{-bt}\cos(\omega t+\phi_1)$ $+\dfrac{1}{2\omega^3(b^2+\omega^2)}\sqrt{U^2+V^2}\;\epsilon^{-bt}\cos(\omega t+\phi_2)$ $R=\left[b(3\omega^2-b^2)+a_2(b^2-\omega^2)-a_1b+a_0\right],\; Q=\omega\left[3b^2-\omega^2-2a_2b+a_1\right]$ $U=2\left[a_0\omega-a_1b\omega+a_2b^2\omega-b\omega^3-\omega b^3\right]$ $V=a_0b+a_1(\omega^2-b^2)+a_2(b^3-b\omega^2)+(\omega^4-b^4)$ $\phi_1=\tan^{-1}\left(\dfrac{Q}{R}\right)-\tan^{-1}\left(\dfrac{\omega}{-b}\right),\; \phi_2=\tan^{-1}\left(\dfrac{V}{U}\right)-2\tan^{-1}\left(\dfrac{\omega}{-b}\right)$
426	$\dfrac{s^3+a_2s^2+a_1s+a_0}{(s+c)\left[(s+b)^2+\omega^2\right]^2}$	$\dfrac{-c^3+a_2c^2-a_1c+a_0}{\left[(b-c)^2+\omega^2\right]^2}\epsilon^{-ct}-\dfrac{1}{2\omega^2}\sqrt{\dfrac{R^2+Q^2}{(c-b)^2+\omega^2}}\;t\epsilon^{-bt}\cos(\omega t+\phi_1)$ $+\dfrac{1}{2\omega^3\left[(c-b)^2+\omega^2\right]}\sqrt{U^2+V^2}\;\epsilon^{-bt}\cos(\omega t+\phi_2)$ $R=\left[b(3\omega^2-b^2)+a_2(b^2-\omega^2)-a_1b+a_0\right],\; Q=\omega\left[3b^2-\omega^2-2a_2b+a_1\right]$ $U=2\left[a_0\omega-a_1b\omega+a_2b^2\omega-b\omega^3+c\omega^3-b^3\omega\right]$ $V=a_0(b-c)+a_1(\omega^2-b^2+bc)+a_2(b^3-b^2c-b\omega^2-c\omega^2)$ $+(\omega^4-b^4+cb^3+3\omega^2cb)$ $\phi_1=\tan^{-1}\left(\dfrac{Q}{R}\right)-\tan^{-1}\left(\dfrac{\omega}{c-b}\right),\; \phi_2=\tan^{-1}\left(\dfrac{V}{U}\right)-2\tan^{-1}\left(\dfrac{\omega}{c-b}\right)$
427	$\dfrac{s^3+a_2s^2+a_1s+a_0}{\left[(s+b)^2+\omega^2\right]\left[(s+c)^2+d^2\right]}$	$\dfrac{1}{\omega}\sqrt{\dfrac{R^2+Q^2}{\left[(c-b)^2+\omega^2-d^2\right]^2+4d^2(c-b)^2}}\;\epsilon^{-bt}\cos(\omega t-\phi_1)$ $+\dfrac{1}{d}\sqrt{\dfrac{T^2+X^2}{\left[(c-b)^2+\omega^2-d^2\right]^2+4d^2(c-b)^2}}\;\epsilon^{-ct}\cos(dt-\phi_2)$ $R=\left[b(3\omega^2-b^2)+a_2(b^2-\omega^2)-a_1b+a_0\right],\; Q=\omega\left[3b^2-\omega^2-2a_2b+a_1\right]$ $T=\left[c(3d^2-c^2)+a_2(c^2-d^2)-a_1c+a_0\right],\; X=d\left[3c^2-d^2-2a_2c+a_1\right]$ $\phi_1=\tan^{-1}\left(\dfrac{R}{Q}\right)+\tan^{-1}\left[\dfrac{2\omega(c-b)}{(c-b)^2-\omega^2+d^2}\right]$ $\phi_2=\tan^{-1}\left(\dfrac{T}{X}\right)+\tan^{-1}\left[\dfrac{2d(b-c)}{(c-b)^2-d^2+\omega^2}\right]$

NO.	F(s)	f(t)
428	$\frac{s^3+a_2s^2+a_1s+a_o}{s[(s+b)^2+\omega^2][(s+c)^2+d^2]}$	$\frac{a_o}{(b^2+\omega^2)(c^2+d^2)} - \frac{1}{\omega}\sqrt{\frac{R^2+Q^2}{(b^2+\omega^2)\{[(c-b)^2+\omega^2-d^2]^2+4d^2(c-b)^2\}}}\,\epsilon^{-bt}\cos(\omega t+\phi_1)$ $-\frac{1}{d}\sqrt{\frac{T^2+X^2}{(c^2+d^2)\{[(c-b)^2+\omega^2-d^2]^2+4d^2(c-b)^2\}}}\,\epsilon^{-ct}\cos(dt+\phi_2)$ $R=[b(3\omega^2-b^2)+a_2(b^2-\omega^2)-a_1b+a_o]$, $Q=\omega[3b^2-\omega^2-2a_2b+a_1]$ $T=[c(3d^2-c^2)+a_2(c^2-d^2)-a_1c+a_o]$, $X=d[3c^2-d^2-2a_2c+a_1]$ $\phi_1=\tan^{-1}\left(\frac{Q}{R}\right)-\tan^{-1}\left(\frac{b}{\omega}\right)-\tan^{-1}\left[\frac{2\omega(c-b)}{(c-b)^2-\omega^2+d^2}\right]$ $\phi_2=\tan^{-1}\left(\frac{X}{T}\right)-\tan^{-1}\left(\frac{c}{d}\right)-\tan^{-1}\left[\frac{2d(b-c)}{(c-b)^2+\omega^2-d^2}\right]$
429	$\frac{s^3+a_2s^2+a_1s+a_o}{(s+f)[(s+b)^2+\omega^2][(s+c)^2+d^2]}$	$\frac{-f^3+a_2f^2-a_1f+a_o}{[(b-f)^2+\omega^2][(c-f)^2+d^2]}\epsilon^{-ft}+\frac{1}{\omega}\sqrt{\frac{R^2+Q^2}{[(f-b)^2+\omega^2]\{[(c-b)^2+\omega^2-d^2]^2+4d^2(c-b)^2\}}}\,\epsilon^{-bt}\cos(\omega t-\phi_1)$ $+\frac{1}{d}\sqrt{\frac{T^2+X^2}{[(f-c)^2+d^2]\{[(c-b)^2+\omega^2-d^2]^2+4d^2(c-b)^2\}}}\,\epsilon^{-ct}\cos(dt-\phi_2)$ $R=[b(3\omega^2-b^2)+a_2(b^2-\omega^2)-a_1b+a_o]$, $Q=\omega[3b^2-\omega^2-2a_2b+a_1]$ $T=[c(3d^2-c^2)+a_2(c^2-d^2)-a_1c+a_o]$, $X=d[3c^2-d^2-2a_2c+a_1]$ $\phi_1=\tan^{-1}\left(\frac{R}{Q}\right)+\tan^{-1}\left(\frac{\omega}{f-b}\right)+\tan^{-1}\left[\frac{2\omega(c-b)}{(c-b)^2-\omega^2+d^2}\right]$ $\phi_2=\tan^{-1}\left(\frac{T}{X}\right)+\tan^{-1}\left(\frac{d}{f-c}\right)+\tan^{-1}\left[\frac{2d(b-c)}{(c-b)^2+\omega^2-d^2}\right]$
430	$\frac{s^4}{(s+b)(s+c)(s+d)(s+f)(s+g)}$	$\frac{b^4}{(c-b)(d-b)(f-b)(g-b)}\epsilon^{-bt}+\frac{c^4}{(b-c)(d-c)(f-c)(g-c)}\epsilon^{-ct}+\frac{d^4}{(b-d)(c-d)(f-d)(g-d)}\epsilon^{-dt}$ $+\frac{f^4}{(b-f)(c-f)(d-f)(g-f)}\epsilon^{-ft}+\frac{g^4}{(b-g)(c-g)(d-g)(f-g)}\epsilon^{-gt}$
431	$\frac{s^4}{(s+b)(s+c)(s+d)(s+f)^2}$	$\frac{b^4}{(c-b)(d-b)(f-b)^2}\epsilon^{-bt}+\frac{c^4}{(b-c)(d-c)(f-c)^2}\epsilon^{-ct}+\frac{d^4}{(b-d)(c-d)(f-d)^2}\epsilon^{-dt}$ $+\frac{f^4}{(b-f)(c-f)(d-f)}t\epsilon^{-ft}-\left[\frac{4f^3}{(b-f)(c-f)(d-f)}\right.$ $\left.+\frac{f^4[(b-f)(c-f)+(b-f)(d-f)+(c-f)(d-f)]}{(b-f)^2(c-f)^2(d-f)^2}\right]\epsilon^{-ft}$
432	$\frac{s^4}{(s+d)(s+b)^2(s+c)^2}$	$\frac{b^4}{(d-b)(c-b)^2}t\epsilon^{-bt}-\left[\frac{4b^3}{(d-b)(c-b)^2}+\frac{b^4(c+2d-3b)}{(c-b)^3(d-b)^2}\right]\epsilon^{-bt}+\frac{c^4}{(d-c)(b-c)^2}t\epsilon^{-ct}$ $-\left[\frac{4c^3}{(d-c)(b-c)^2}+\frac{c^4(b+2d-3c)}{(b-c)^3(d-c)^2}\right]\epsilon^{-ct}+\frac{d^4}{(b-d)^2(c-d)^2}\epsilon^{-dt}$

NO.	F(s)	f(t)
433	$\frac{s^4}{(s+b)(s+c)(s+d)(s^2+\omega^2)}$	$\frac{b^4}{(c-b)(d-b)(b^2+\omega^2)}\epsilon^{-bt}+\frac{c^4}{(b-c)(d-c)(c^2+\omega^2)}\epsilon^{-ct}+\frac{d^4}{(b-d)(c-d)(d^2+\omega^2)}\epsilon^{-dt}$ $+\frac{\omega^3}{\sqrt{(b^2+\omega^2)(c^2+\omega^2)(d^2+\omega^2)}}\sin(\omega t-\phi)$ $\phi=\tan^{-1}\left(\frac{\omega}{b}\right)+\tan^{-1}\left(\frac{\omega}{c}\right)+\tan^{-1}\left(\frac{\omega}{d}\right)$
434	$\frac{s^4}{(s+c)(s+b)^2(s^2+\omega^2)}$	$\frac{c^4}{(b-c)^2(c^2+\omega^2)}\epsilon^{-ct}+\frac{b^4}{(c-b)(b^2+\omega^2)}t\epsilon^{-bt}-\left[\frac{4b^3}{(c-b)(b^2+\omega^2)}+\frac{b^4(\omega^2+3b^2-2bc)}{(c-b)^2(b^2+\omega^2)^2}\right]\epsilon^{-bt}$ $+\frac{1}{(b^2+\omega^2)}\frac{\omega^3}{\sqrt{c^2+\omega^2}}\sin(\omega t-\phi)$; $\phi=\tan^{-1}\left(\frac{\omega}{c}\right)+2\tan^{-1}\left(\frac{\omega}{b}\right)$
435	$\frac{s^4}{(s+c)(s^2+b^2)(s^2+\omega^2)}$	$\frac{c^4}{(c^2+b^2)(c^2+\omega^2)}\epsilon^{-ct}+\frac{1}{(\omega^2-b^2)}\frac{b^3}{\sqrt{c^2+b^2}}\sin(bt-\phi_1)$ $+\frac{1}{(b^2-\omega^2)}\frac{\omega^3}{\sqrt{c^2+\omega^2}}\sin(\omega t-\phi_2)$ $\phi_1=\tan^{-1}\left(\frac{b}{c}\right)$, $\phi_2=\tan^{-1}\left(\frac{\omega}{c}\right)$
436	$\frac{s^4}{(s+b)(s^2+\omega^2)^2}$	$\frac{b^4}{(b^2+\omega^2)^2}\epsilon^{-bt}-\frac{1}{2}\frac{\omega^2}{\sqrt{b^2+\omega^2}}t\cos(\omega t+\phi_1)+\frac{\omega\sqrt{4\omega^2+9b^2}}{2(b^2+\omega^2)}\cos(\omega t+\phi_2)$ $\phi_1=-\tan^{-1}\left(\frac{\omega}{b}\right)$, $\phi_2=-2\tan^{-1}\left(\frac{\omega}{b}\right)+\tan^{-1}\left(\frac{3b}{-2\omega}\right)$
437	$\frac{s^4}{(s+c)(s+d)^2\left[(s+b)^2+\omega^2\right]}$	$\frac{c^4}{(d-c)^2\left[(b-c)^2+\omega^2\right]}\epsilon^{-ct}+\frac{1}{\omega\left[(d-b)^2+\omega^2\right]}\sqrt{\frac{(b^4-6b^2\omega^2+\omega^4)^2+16b^2\omega^2(b^2-\omega^2)^2}{(c-b)^2+\omega^2}}\epsilon^{-bt}\cos(\omega t-\phi)$ $+\frac{d^4}{(c-d)\left[(b-d)^2+\omega^2\right]}t\epsilon^{-dt}-\left[\frac{4d^3}{(c-d)\left[(b-d)^2+\omega^2\right]}\right.$ $\left.+\frac{d^4\left[(b-d)^2+\omega^2+2(c-d)(b-d)\right]}{(c-d)^2\left[(b-d)^2+\omega^2\right]^2}\right]\epsilon^{-dt}$ $\phi=\tan^{-1}\left[\frac{b^4-6b^2\omega^2+\omega^4}{-4b\omega(b^2-\omega^2)}\right]+\tan^{-1}\left(\frac{\omega}{c-b}\right)+2\tan^{-1}\left(\frac{\omega}{d-b}\right)$
438	$\frac{s^4}{(s+c)(s+d)(s+f)\left[(s+b)^2+\omega^2\right]}$	$\frac{c^4}{(d-c)(f-c)\left[(b-c)^2+\omega^2\right]}\epsilon^{-ct}+\frac{d^4}{(c-d)(f-d)\left[(b-d)^2+\omega^2\right]}\epsilon^{-dt}+\frac{f^4}{(c-f)(d-f)\left[(b-f)^2+\omega^2\right]}\epsilon^{-ft}$ $+\frac{1}{\omega}\sqrt{\frac{(b^4-6b^2\omega^2+\omega^4)^2+16b^2\omega^2(b^2-\omega^2)^2}{\left[(c-b)^2+\omega^2\right]\left[(d-b)^2+\omega^2\right]\left[(f-b)^2+\omega^2\right]}}\epsilon^{-bt}\cos(\omega t-\phi)$ $\phi=\tan^{-1}\left[\frac{b^4-6b^2\omega^2+\omega^4}{-4b\omega(b^2-\omega^2)}\right]+\tan^{-1}\left(\frac{\omega}{c-b}\right)+\tan^{-1}\left(\frac{\omega}{d-b}\right)$ $+\tan^{-1}\left(\frac{\omega}{f-b}\right)$

NO.	F(s)	f(t)
439	$\frac{s^4}{(s+d)(s^2+c^2)\left[(s+b)^2+\omega^2\right]}$	$\frac{d^4}{(d^2+c^2)\left[(b-d)^2+\omega^2\right]}\epsilon^{-dt}+\frac{c^3}{\sqrt{(d^2+c^2)\left[(b^2+\omega^2-c^2)^2+4b^2c^2\right]}}\sin(ct-\phi_1)$ $+\frac{1}{\omega}\sqrt{\frac{(b^4-6b^2\omega^2+\omega^4)^2+16b^2\omega^2(b^2-\omega^2)^2}{\left[(d-b)^2+\omega^2\right]\left[(b^2+\omega^2-c^2)^2+4b^2c^2\right]}}\epsilon^{-bt}\cos(\omega t-\phi_2)$ $\phi_1=\tan^{-1}\left(\frac{c}{d}\right)+\tan^{-1}\left(\frac{2bc}{b^2+\omega^2-c^2}\right)$ $\phi_2=\tan^{-1}\left[\frac{b^4-6b^2\omega^2+\omega^4}{-4b\omega(b^2-\omega^2)}\right]+\tan^{-1}\left(\frac{\omega}{d-b}\right)-\tan^{-1}\left(\frac{2b\omega}{b^2-\omega^2+c^2}\right)$
440	$\frac{s^4}{(s+c)\left[(s+b)^2+\omega^2\right]^2}$	$\frac{c^4}{\left[(b-c)^2+\omega^2\right]^2}\epsilon^{-ct}-\frac{1}{2\omega^2}\sqrt{\frac{(b^4-6b^2\omega^2+\omega^4)^2+16b^2\omega^2(b^2-\omega^2)^2}{(c-b)^2+\omega^2}}\,t\epsilon^{-bt}\cos(\omega t+\phi_1)$ $+\frac{1}{2\omega^3\left[(c-b)^2+\omega^2\right]}\sqrt{T^2+X^2}\,\epsilon^{-bt}\cos(\omega t+\phi_2)$ $T=2\omega\left[b^4-\omega^4+4b^2\omega^2-4bc\omega^2\right]$ $X=\left[b^5-b^4c+2b^3\omega^2-6b^2\omega^2c-7b\omega^4+3\omega^4c\right]$ $\phi_1=\tan^{-1}\left[\frac{-4b\omega(b^2-\omega^2)}{b^4-6b^2\omega^2+\omega^4}\right]-\tan^{-1}\left(\frac{\omega}{c-b}\right)$ $\phi_2=\tan^{-1}\left(\frac{X}{T}\right)-2\tan^{-1}\left(\frac{\omega}{c-b}\right)$
441	$\frac{s^4}{(s+f)\left[(s+b)^2+\omega^2\right]\left[(s+c)^2+d^2\right]}$	$\frac{f^4}{\left[(b-f)^2+\omega^2\right]\left[(c-f)^2+d^2\right]}\epsilon^{-ft}+\frac{1}{\omega}\sqrt{\frac{(b^4-6b^2\omega^2+\omega^4)^2+16b^2\omega^2(b^2-\omega^2)^2}{\left[(f-b)^2+\omega^2\right]\left\{\left[(c-b)^2+\omega^2-d^2\right]^2+4d^2(c-b)^2\right\}}}\epsilon^{-bt}\cos(\omega t-\phi_1)$ $+\frac{1}{d}\sqrt{\frac{(c^4-6c^2d^2+d^4)^2+16c^2d^2(c^2-d^2)^2}{\left[(f-c)^2+d^2\right]\left\{\left[(c-b)^2+\omega^2-d^2\right]^2+4d^2(c-b)^2\right\}}}\epsilon^{-ct}\cos(dt-\phi_2)$ $\phi_1=\tan^{-1}\left[\frac{b^4-6b^2\omega^2+\omega^4}{-4b\omega(b^2-\omega^2)}\right]+\tan^{-1}\left(\frac{\omega}{f-b}\right)+\tan^{-1}\left[\frac{2\omega(c-b)}{(c-b)^2-\omega^2+d^2}\right]$ $\phi_2=\tan^{-1}\left[\frac{c^4-6c^2d^2+d^4}{-4cd(c^2-d^2)}\right]+\tan^{-1}\left(\frac{d}{f-c}\right)+\tan^{-1}\left[\frac{2d(b-c)}{(c-b)^2+\omega^2-d^2}\right]$
442	$\frac{s^4+a_3s^3+a_2s^2+a_1s+a_0}{s^2(s+b)(s+c)(s+d)}$	$\frac{a_0}{bcd}t+\left[\frac{a_1}{bcd}-\frac{a_0(bc+bd+cd)}{b^2c^2d^2}\right]+\frac{b^4-a_3b^3+a_2b^2-a_1b+a_0}{b^2(c-b)(d-b)}\epsilon^{-bt}$ $+\frac{c^4-a_3c^3+a_2c^2-a_1c+a_0}{c^2(b-c)(d-c)}\epsilon^{-ct}+\frac{d^4-a_3d^3+a_2d^2-a_1d+a_0}{d^2(b-d)(c-d)}\epsilon^{-dt}$
443	$\frac{s^4+a_3s^3+a_2s^2+a_1s+a_0}{s(s+b)(s+c)(s+d)(s+f)}$	$\frac{a_0}{bcdf}-\frac{b^4-a_3b^3+a_2b^2-a_1b+a_0}{b(c-b)(d-b)(f-b)}\epsilon^{-bt}-\frac{c^4-a_3c^3+a_2c^2-a_1c+a_0}{c(b-c)(d-c)(f-c)}\epsilon^{-ct}$ $-\frac{d^4-a_3d^3+a_2d^2-a_1d+a_0}{d(b-d)(c-d)(f-d)}\epsilon^{-dt}-\frac{f^4-a_3f^3+a_2f^2-a_1f+a_0}{f(b-f)(c-f)(d-f)}\epsilon^{-ft}$

NO.	F(s)	f(t)
444	$\dfrac{s^4+a_3s^3+a_2s^2+a_1s+a_0}{(s+b)(s+c)(s+d)(s+f)(s+g)}$	$\dfrac{b^4-a_3b^3+a_2b^2-a_1b+a_0}{(c-b)(d-b)(f-b)(g-b)}\epsilon^{-bt}+\dfrac{c^4-a_3c^3+a_2c^2-a_1c+a_0}{(b-c)(d-c)(f-c)(g-c)}\epsilon^{-ct}+\dfrac{d^4-a_3d^3+a_2d^2-a_1d+a_0}{(b-d)(c-d)(f-d)(g-d)}\epsilon^{-dt}+\dfrac{f^4-a_3f^3+a_2f^2-a_1f+a_0}{(b-f)(c-f)(d-f)(g-f)}\epsilon^{-ft}+\dfrac{g^4-a_3g^3+a_2g^2-a_1g+a_0}{(b-g)(c-g)(d-g)(f-g)}\epsilon^{-gt}$
445	$\dfrac{s^4+a_3s^3+a_2s^2+a_1s+a_0}{s(s+b)(s+c)(s+d)^2}$	$\dfrac{a_0}{bcd^2}-\dfrac{b^4-a_3b^3+a_2b^2-a_1b+a_0}{b(c-b)(d-b)^2}\epsilon^{-bt}-\dfrac{c^4-a_3c^3+a_2c^2-a_1c+a_0}{c(b-c)(d-c)^2}\epsilon^{-ct}-\dfrac{d^4-a_3d^3+a_2d^2-a_1d+a_0}{d(b-d)(c-d)}t\epsilon^{-dt}-\left[\dfrac{-4d^3+3a_3d^2-2a_2d+a_1}{d(b-d)(c-d)}+\dfrac{(d^4-a_3d^3+a_2d^2-a_1d+a_0)[(b-d)(c-d)-d(b-d)-d(c-d)]}{d^2(b-d)^2(c-d)^2}\right]\epsilon^{-dt}$
446	$\dfrac{s^4+a_3s^3+a_2s^2+a_1s+a_0}{(s+b)(s+c)(s+d)(s+f)^2}$	$\dfrac{b^4-a_3b^3+a_2b^2-a_1b+a_0}{(c-b)(d-b)(f-b)^2}\epsilon^{-bt}+\dfrac{c^4-a_3c^3+a_2c^2-a_1c+a_0}{(b-c)(d-c)(f-c)^2}\epsilon^{-ct}+\dfrac{d^4-a_3d^3+a_2d^2-a_1d+a_0}{(b-d)(c-d)(f-d)^2}\epsilon^{-dt}+\dfrac{f^4-a_3f^3+a_2f^2-a_1f+a_0}{(b-f)(c-f)(d-f)}t\epsilon^{-ft}+\left[\dfrac{-4f^3+3a_3f^2-2a_2f+a_1}{(b-f)(c-f)(d-f)}-\dfrac{(f^4-a_3f^3+a_2f^2-a_1f+a_0)[(b-f)(c-f)+(b-f)(d-f)+(c-f)(d-f)]}{(b-f)^2(c-f)^2(d-f)^2}\right]\epsilon^{-ft}$
447	$\dfrac{s^4+a_3s^3+a_2s^2+a_1s+a_0}{s^2(s+b)(s+c)^2}$	$\dfrac{a_0}{bc^2}t+\left[\dfrac{a_1}{bc^2}-\dfrac{a_0(2b+c)}{b^2c^3}\right]+\dfrac{c^4-a_3c^3+a_2c^2-a_1c+a_0}{c^2(b-c)}t\epsilon^{-ct}+\left[\dfrac{-4c^3+3a_3c^2-2a_2c+a_1}{c^2(b-c)}+\dfrac{(c^4-a_3c^3+a_2c^2-a_1c+a_0)(2b-3c)}{c^3(b-c)^2}\right]\epsilon^{-ct}+\dfrac{b^4-a_3b^3+a_2b^2-a_1b+a_0}{b^2(c-b)^2}\epsilon^{-bt}$
448	$\dfrac{s^4+a_3s^3+a_2s^2+a_1s+a_0}{s(s+b)^2(s+c)^2}$	$\dfrac{a_0}{b^2c^2}-\dfrac{b^4-a_3b^3+a_2b^2-a_1b+a_0}{b(c-b)^2}t\epsilon^{-bt}-\left[\dfrac{-4b^3+3a_3b^2-2a_2b+a_1}{b(c-b)^2}+\dfrac{(b^4-a_3b^3+a_2b^2-a_1b+a_0)(c-3b)}{b^2(c-b)^3}\right]\epsilon^{-bt}-\dfrac{c^4-a_3c^3+a_2c^2-a_1c+a_0}{c(b-c)^2}t\epsilon^{-ct}-\left[\dfrac{-4c^3+3a_3c^2-2a_2c+a_1}{c(b-c)^2}+\dfrac{(c^4-a_3c^3+a_2c^2-a_1c+a_0)(b-3c)}{c^2(b-c)^3}\right]\epsilon^{-ct}$
449	$\dfrac{s^4+a_3s^3+a_2s^2+a_1s+a_0}{(s+d)(s+b)^2(s+c)^2}$	$\dfrac{d^4-a_3d^3+a_2d^2-a_1d+a_0}{(b-d)^2(c-d)^2}\epsilon^{-dt}+\dfrac{b^4-a_3b^3+a_2b^2-a_1b+a_0}{(d-b)(c-b)^2}t\epsilon^{-bt}+\left[\dfrac{-4b^3+3a_3b^2-2a_2b+a_1}{(d-b)(c-b)^2}-\dfrac{(b^4-a_3b^3+a_2b^2-a_1b+a_0)(c+2d-3b)}{(d-b)^2(c-b)^3}\right]\epsilon^{-bt}+\dfrac{c^4-a_3c^3+a_2c^2-a_1c+a_0}{(d-c)(b-c)^2}t\epsilon^{-ct}+\left[\dfrac{-4c^3+3a_3c^2-2a_2c+a_1}{(d-c)(b-c)^2}-\dfrac{(c^4-a_3c^3+a_2c^2-a_1c+a_0)(b+2d-3c)}{(d-c)^2(b-c)^3}\right]\epsilon^{-ct}$

NO.	F(s)	f(t)
450	$\dfrac{s^4+a_3s^3+a_2s^2+a_1s+a_0}{s^2(s+b)(s^2+\omega^2)}$	$\dfrac{a_0}{b\omega^2}t+\left[\dfrac{a_1}{b\omega^2}-\dfrac{a_0}{b^2\omega^2}\right]+\dfrac{b^4-a_3b^3+a_2b^2-a_1b+a_0}{b^2(b^2+\omega^2)}\epsilon^{-bt}$ $-\dfrac{1}{\omega^3}\sqrt{\dfrac{(\omega^4-a_2\omega^2+a_0)^2+\omega^2(a_1-a_3\omega^2)^2}{b^2+\omega^2}}\cos(\omega t-\phi)$ $\phi=\tan^{-1}\left[\dfrac{\omega^4-a_2\omega^2+a_0}{\omega(a_1-a_3\omega^2)}\right]+\tan^{-1}\left(\dfrac{\omega}{b}\right)$
451	$\dfrac{s^4+a_3s^3+a_2s^2+a_1s+a_0}{s(s+b)(s+c)(s^2+\omega^2)}$	$\dfrac{a_0}{bc\omega^2}-\dfrac{b^4-a_3b^3+a_2b^2-a_1b+a_0}{b(c-b)(b^2+\omega^2)}\epsilon^{-bt}-\dfrac{c^4-a_3c^3+a_2c^2-a_1c+a_0}{c(b-c)(c^2+\omega^2)}\epsilon^{-ct}$ $-\dfrac{1}{\omega^2}\sqrt{\dfrac{(\omega^4-a_2\omega^2+a_0)^2+\omega^2(a_1-a_3\omega^2)^2}{(b^2+\omega^2)(c^2+\omega^2)}}\cos(\omega t+\phi)$ $\phi=\tan^{-1}\left[\dfrac{\omega(a_1-a_3\omega^2)}{\omega^4-a_2\omega^2+a_0}\right]-\tan^{-1}\left(\dfrac{\omega}{b}\right)-\tan^{-1}\left(\dfrac{\omega}{c}\right)$
452	$\dfrac{s^4+a_3s^3+a_2s^2+a_1s+a_0}{(s+b)(s+c)(s+d)(s^2+\omega^2)}$	$\dfrac{b^4-a_3b^3+a_2b^2-a_1b+a_0}{(c-b)(d-b)(b^2+\omega^2)}\epsilon^{-bt}+\dfrac{c^4-a_3c^3+a_2c^2-a_1c+a_0}{(b-c)(d-c)(c^2+\omega^2)}\epsilon^{-ct}+\dfrac{d^4-a_3d^3+a_2d^2-a_1d+a_0}{(b-d)(c-d)(d^2+\omega^2)}\epsilon^{-dt}$ $+\dfrac{1}{\omega}\sqrt{\dfrac{(\omega^4-a_2\omega^2+a_0)^2+\omega^2(a_1-a_3\omega^2)^2}{(b^2+\omega^2)(c^2+\omega^2)(d^2+\omega^2)}}\cos(\omega t-\phi)$ $\phi=\tan^{-1}\left[\dfrac{\omega^4-a_2\omega^2+a_0}{\omega(a_1-a_3\omega^2)}\right]+\tan^{-1}\left(\dfrac{\omega}{b}\right)+\tan^{-1}\left(\dfrac{\omega}{c}\right)+\tan^{-1}\left(\dfrac{\omega}{d}\right)$
453	$\dfrac{s^4+a_3s^3+a_2s^2+a_1s+a_0}{s(s+b)^2(s^2+\omega^2)}$	$\dfrac{a_0}{b^2\omega^2}-\dfrac{b^4-a_3b^3+a_2b^2-a_1b+a_0}{b(b^2+\omega^2)}t\epsilon^{-bt}-\left[\dfrac{-4b^3+3a_3b^2-2a_2b+a_1}{b(b^2+\omega^2)}\right.$ $\left.+\dfrac{(b^4-a_3b^3+a_2b^2-a_1b+a_0)(\omega^2+3b^2)}{b^2(b^2+\omega^2)^2}\right]\epsilon^{-bt}$ $-\dfrac{1}{\omega^2(b^2+\omega^2)}\sqrt{(\omega^4-a_2\omega^2+a_0)^2+\omega^2(a_1-a_3\omega^2)^2}\cos(\omega t+\phi)$ $\phi=\tan^{-1}\left[\dfrac{\omega(a_1-a_3\omega^2)}{\omega^4-a_2\omega^2+a_0}\right]-2\tan^{-1}\left(\dfrac{\omega}{b}\right)$
454	$\dfrac{s^4+a_3s^3+a_2s^2+a_1s+a_0}{(s+c)(s+b)^2(s^2+\omega^2)}$	$\dfrac{c^4-a_3c^3+a_2c^2-a_1c+a_0}{(b-c)^2(c^2+\omega^2)}\epsilon^{-ct}+\dfrac{b^4-a_3b^3+a_2b^2-a_1b+a_0}{(c-b)(b^2+\omega^2)}t\epsilon^{-bt}$ $+\left[\dfrac{-4b^3+3a_3b^2-2a_2b+a_1}{(c-b)(b^2+\omega^2)}-\dfrac{(b^4-a_3b^3+a_2b^2-a_1b+a_0)(3b^2+\omega^2-2bc)}{(c-b)^2(b^2+\omega^2)^2}\right]\epsilon^{-bt}$ $+\dfrac{1}{\omega(b^2+\omega^2)}\sqrt{\dfrac{(\omega^4-a_2\omega^2+a_0)^2+\omega^2(a_1-a_3\omega^2)^2}{c^2+\omega^2}}\cos(\omega t-\phi)$ $\phi=\tan^{-1}\left[\dfrac{\omega^4-a_2\omega^2+a_0}{\omega(a_1-a_3\omega^2)}\right]+\tan^{-1}\left(\dfrac{\omega}{c}\right)+2\tan^{-1}\left(\dfrac{\omega}{b}\right)$

NO.	F(s)	f(t)
455	$\dfrac{s^4+a_3s^3+a_2s^2+a_1s+a_0}{s(s^2+b^2)(s^2+\omega^2)}$	$\dfrac{a_0}{b^2\omega^2}-\dfrac{1}{b^2(\omega^2-b^2)}\sqrt{(b^4-a_2b^2+a_0)^2+b^2(a_1-a_3b^2)^2}\ \cos(bt+\phi_1)$ $-\dfrac{1}{\omega^2(b^2-\omega^2)}\sqrt{(\omega^4-a_2\omega^2+a_0)^2+\omega^2(a_1-a_3\omega^2)^2}\ \cos(\omega t+\phi_2)$ $\phi_1=\tan^{-1}\left[\dfrac{b(a_1-a_3b^2)}{b^4-a_2b^2+a_0}\right],\ \phi_2=\tan^{-1}\left[\dfrac{\omega(a_1-a_3\omega^2)}{\omega^4-a_2\omega^2+a_0}\right]$
456	$\dfrac{s^4+a_3s^3+a_2s^2+a_1s+a_0}{(s+c)(s^2+b^2)(s^2+\omega^2)}$	$\dfrac{c^4-a_3c^3+a_2c^2-a_1c+a_0}{(c^2+b^2)(c^2+\omega^2)}\epsilon^{-ct}+\dfrac{1}{b(\omega^2-b^2)}\sqrt{\dfrac{(b^4-a_2b^2+a_0)^2+b^2(a_1-a_3b^2)^2}{c^2+b^2}}\cos(bt-\phi_1)$ $+\dfrac{1}{\omega(b^2-\omega^2)}\sqrt{\dfrac{(\omega^4-a_2\omega^2+a_0)^2+\omega^2(a_1-a_3\omega^2)^2}{c^2+\omega^2}}\ \cos(\omega t-\phi_2)$ $\phi_1=\tan^{-1}\left[\dfrac{b^4-a_2b^2+a_0}{b(a_1-a_3b^2)}\right]+\tan^{-1}\left(\dfrac{b}{c}\right),\ \phi_2=\tan^{-1}\left[\dfrac{\omega^4-a_2\omega^2+a_0}{\omega(a_1-a_3\omega^2)}\right]+\tan^{-1}\left(\dfrac{\omega}{c}\right)$
457	$\dfrac{s^4+a_3s^3+a_2s^2+a_1s+a_0}{s(s^2+\omega^2)^2}$	$\dfrac{a_0}{\omega^4}-\dfrac{1}{2\omega^3}\sqrt{(\omega^4-a_2\omega^2+a_0)^2+\omega^2(a_1-a_3\omega^2)^2}\ t\cos(\omega t-\phi_1)$ $-\dfrac{1}{2\omega^4}\sqrt{4(a_0-\omega^4)^2+\omega^2(a_1+a_3\omega^2)^2}\ \ \cos(\omega t+\phi_2)$ $\phi_1=\tan^{-1}\left[\dfrac{\omega^4-a_2\omega^2+a_0}{\omega(a_1-a_3\omega^2)}\right],\ \phi_2=\tan^{-1}\left[\dfrac{\omega(a_1+a_3\omega^2)}{2(a_0-\omega^4)}\right]$
458	$\dfrac{s^4+a_3s^3+a_2s^2+a_1s+a_0}{(s+b)(s^2+\omega^2)^2}$	$\dfrac{b^4-a_3b^3+a_2b^2-a_1b+a_0}{(b^2+\omega^2)^2}\epsilon^{-bt}-\dfrac{1}{2\omega^2}\sqrt{\dfrac{(\omega^4-a_2\omega^2+a_0)^2+\omega^2(a_1-a_3\omega^2)^2}{b^2+\omega^2}}\ t\cos(\omega t+\phi_1)$ $+\dfrac{1}{2\omega^3(b^2+\omega^2)}\sqrt{\omega^2\left[2a_3b\omega^2+2a_0-2\omega^4\right]^2+\left[(a_3+3b)\omega^4+(a_1-ba_2)\omega^2-a_0b\right]^2}\cos(\omega t+\phi_2)$ $\phi_1=\tan^{-1}\left[\dfrac{\omega(a_1-a_3\omega^2)}{\omega^4-a_2\omega^2+a_0}\right]-\tan^{-1}\left(\dfrac{\omega}{b}\right)$ $\phi_2=\tan^{-1}\left[\dfrac{(a_3+3b)\omega^4+(a_1-ba_2)\omega^2-a_0b}{\omega(2a_3b\omega^2+2a_0-2\omega^4)}\right]-2\tan^{-1}\left(\dfrac{\omega}{b}\right)$
459	$\dfrac{s^4+a_3s^3+a_2s^2+a_1s+a_0}{s^2(s+c)[(s+b)^2+\omega^2]}$	$\dfrac{a_0}{c(b^2+\omega^2)}t+\left[\dfrac{a_1}{c(b^2+\omega^2)}-\dfrac{a_0(b^2+\omega^2+2bc)}{c^2(b^2+\omega^2)^2}\right]+\dfrac{c^4-a_3c^3+a_2c^2-a_1c+a_0}{c^2[(b-c)^2+\omega^2]}\epsilon^{-ct}$ $+\dfrac{1}{\omega(b^2+\omega^2)}\sqrt{\dfrac{R^2+Q^2}{(b-c)^2+\omega^2}}\ \epsilon^{-bt}\cos(\omega t-\phi)$ $R=\left[(b^4+\omega^4-6b^2\omega^2)+a_3b(3\omega^2-b^2)+a_2(b^2-\omega^2)-a_1b+a_0\right]$ $Q=\left[4b\omega(\omega^2-b^2)+a_3\omega(3b^2-\omega^2)-a_2 2b\omega+a_1\omega\right]$ $\phi=\tan^{-1}\left(\dfrac{R}{Q}\right)+\tan^{-1}\left(\dfrac{\omega}{c-b}\right)-2\tan^{-1}\left(\dfrac{\omega}{b}\right)$

NO.	F(s)	f(t)
460	$\dfrac{s^4+a_3s^3+a_2s^2+a_1s+a_0}{s(s+c)(s+d)[(s+b)^2+\omega^2]}$	$\dfrac{a_0}{cd(b^2+\omega^2)}-\dfrac{c^4-a_3c^3+a_2c^2-a_1c+a_0}{c(d-c)[(b-c)^2+\omega^2]}\epsilon^{-ct}-\dfrac{d^4-a_3d^3+a_2d^2-a_1d+a_0}{d(c-d)[(b-d)^2+\omega^2]}\epsilon^{-dt}$ $-\dfrac{1}{\omega}\sqrt{\dfrac{R^2+Q^2}{(b^2+\omega^2)[(c-b)^2+\omega^2][(d-b)^2+\omega^2]}}\,\epsilon^{-bt}\cos(\omega t+\phi)$ $R=\left[(b^4+\omega^4-6b^2\omega^2)+a_3b(3\omega^2-b^2)+a_2(b^2-\omega^2)-a_1b+a_0\right]$ $Q=\left[4b\omega(\omega^2-b^2)+a_3\omega(3b^2-\omega^2)-a_2 2b\omega+a_1\omega\right]$ $\phi=\tan^{-1}\left(\dfrac{Q}{R}\right)-\tan^{-1}\left(\dfrac{b}{\omega}\right)-\tan^{-1}\left(\dfrac{\omega}{c-b}\right)-\tan^{-1}\left(\dfrac{\omega}{d-b}\right)$
461	$\dfrac{s^4+a_3s^3+a_2s^2+a_1s+a_0}{s(s+c)^2[(s+b)^2+\omega^2]}$	$\dfrac{a_0}{c^2(b^2+\omega^2)}-\dfrac{c^4-a_3c^3+a_2c^2-a_1c+a_0}{c[(b-c)^2+\omega^2]}t\epsilon^{-ct}-\left[\dfrac{-4c^3+3a_3c^2-2a_2c+a_1}{c[(b-c)^2+\omega^2]}\right.$ $\left.+\dfrac{[(b-c)^2+\omega^2-2c(b-c)](c^4-a_3c^3+a_2c^2-a_1c+a_0)}{c^2[(b-c)^2+\omega^2]^2}\right]\epsilon^{-ct}$ $-\dfrac{1}{\omega[(c-b)^2+\omega^2]}\sqrt{\dfrac{R^2+Q^2}{(b^2+\omega^2)}}\,\epsilon^{-bt}\cos(\omega t+\phi)$ $R=\left[(b^4+\omega^4-6b^2\omega^2)+a_3b(3\omega^2-b^2)+a_2(b^2-\omega^2)-a_1b+a_0\right]$ $Q=\left[4b\omega(\omega^2-b^2)+a_3\omega(3b^2-\omega^2)-a_2 2b\omega+a_1\omega\right]$ $\phi=\tan^{-1}\left(\dfrac{Q}{R}\right)-\tan^{-1}\left(\dfrac{b}{\omega}\right)-2\tan^{-1}\left(\dfrac{\omega}{c-b}\right)$
462	$\dfrac{s^4+a_3s^3+a_2s^2+a_1s+a_0}{(s+c)(s+d)^2[(s+b)^2+\omega^2]}$	$\dfrac{c^4-a_3c^3+a_2c^2-a_1c+a_0}{(d-c)^2[(b-c)^2+\omega^2]}\epsilon^{-ct}+\dfrac{1}{\omega[(d-b)^2+\omega^2]}\sqrt{\dfrac{R^2+Q^2}{(c-b)^2+\omega^2}}\,\epsilon^{-bt}\cos(\omega t-\phi)$ $+\dfrac{d^4-a_3d^3+a_2d^2-a_1d+a_0}{(c-d)[(b-d)^2+\omega^2]}t\epsilon^{-dt}+\left[\dfrac{-4d^3+3a_3d^2-2a_2d+a_1}{(c-d)[(b-d)^2+\omega^2]}\right.$ $\left.-\dfrac{(d^4-a_3d^3+a_2d^2-a_1d+a_0)[(b-d)^2+\omega^2+2(c-d)(b-d)]}{(c-d)^2[(b-d)^2+\omega^2]^2}\right]\epsilon^{-dt}$ $R=\left[(b^4+\omega^4-6b^2\omega^2)+a_3b(3\omega^2-b^2)+a_2(b^2-\omega^2)-a_1b+a_0\right]$ $Q=\left[4b\omega(\omega^2-b^2)+a_3\omega(3b^2-\omega^2)-a_2 2b\omega+a_1\omega\right]$ $\phi=\tan^{-1}\left(\dfrac{R}{Q}\right)+\tan^{-1}\left(\dfrac{\omega}{c-b}\right)+2\tan^{-1}\left(\dfrac{\omega}{d-b}\right)$

NO.	F(s)	f(t)
463	$\dfrac{s^4+a_3s^3+a_2s^2+a_1s+a_0}{(s+c)(s+d)(s+f)[(s+b)^2+\omega^2]}$	$\dfrac{c^4-a_3c^3+a_2c^2-a_1c+a_0}{(d-c)(f-c)[(b-c)^2+\omega^2]}\epsilon^{-ct}+\dfrac{d^4-a_3d^3+a_2d^2-a_1d+a_0}{(c-d)(f-d)[(b-d)^2+\omega^2]}\epsilon^{-dt}$ $+\dfrac{f^4-a_3f^3+a_2f^2-a_1f+a_0}{(c-f)(d-f)[(b-f)^2+\omega^2]}\epsilon^{-ft}+\dfrac{1}{\omega}\sqrt{\dfrac{R^2+Q^2}{[(c-b)^2+\omega^2][(d-b)^2+\omega^2][(f-b)^2+\omega^2]}}\epsilon^{-bt}\cos(\omega t-\phi)$ $R=[(b^4+\omega^4-6b^2\omega^2)+a_3b(3\omega^2-b^2)+a_2(b^2-\omega^2)-a_1b+a_0]$ $Q=[4b\omega(\omega^2-b^2)+a_3\omega(3b^2-\omega^2)-a_22b\omega+a_1\omega]$ $\phi=\tan^{-1}\left(\dfrac{R}{Q}\right)+\tan^{-1}\left(\dfrac{\omega}{c-b}\right)+\tan^{-1}\left(\dfrac{\omega}{d-b}\right)+\tan^{-1}\left(\dfrac{\omega}{f-b}\right)$
464	$\dfrac{s^4+a_3s^3+a_2s^2+a_1s+a_0}{s(s^2+c^2)[(s+b)^2+\omega^2]}$	$\dfrac{a_0}{c^2(b^2+\omega^2)}-\dfrac{1}{c^2}\sqrt{\dfrac{(c^4-a_2c^2+a_0)^2+c^2(a_1-a_3c^2)^2}{(b^2+\omega^2-c^2)^2+4b^2c^2}}\cos(ct+\phi_1)$ $-\dfrac{1}{\omega}\sqrt{\dfrac{R^2+Q^2}{(b^2+\omega^2)[(b^2+\omega^2-c^2)^2+4b^2c^2]}}\epsilon^{-bt}\cos(\omega t+\phi_2)$ $R=[(b^4+\omega^4-6b^2\omega^2)+a_3b(3\omega^2-b^2)+a_2(b^2-\omega^2)-a_1b+a_0]$ $Q=[4b\omega(\omega^2-b^2)+a_3\omega(3b^2-\omega^2)-a_22b\omega+a_1\omega]$ $\phi_1=\tan^{-1}\left[\dfrac{c(a_1-a_3c^2)}{c^4-a_2c^2+a_0}\right]-\tan^{-1}\left(\dfrac{2bc}{b^2+\omega^2-c^2}\right)$ $\phi_2=\tan^{-1}\left(\dfrac{Q}{R}\right)-\tan^{-1}\left(\dfrac{b^2-\omega^2+c^2}{2b\omega}\right)+\tan^{-1}\left(\dfrac{\omega}{b}\right)$
465	$\dfrac{s^4+a_3s^3+a_2s^2+a_1s+a_0}{(s+d)(s^2+c^2)[(s+b)^2+\omega^2]}$	$\dfrac{1}{c}\sqrt{\dfrac{(c^4-a_2c^2+a_0)^2+c^2(a_1-a_3c^2)^2}{(d^2+c^2)[(b^2+\omega^2-c^2)^2+4b^2c^2]}}\cos(ct-\phi_1)+\dfrac{d^4-a_3d^3+a_2d^2-a_1d+a_0}{(d^2+c^2)[(b-d)^2+\omega^2]}\epsilon^{-dt}$ $+\dfrac{1}{\omega}\sqrt{\dfrac{R^2+Q^2}{[(d-b)^2+\omega^2][(b^2+\omega^2-c^2)^2+4b^2c^2]}}\epsilon^{-bt}\cos(\omega t-\phi_2)$ $R=[(b^4+\omega^4-6b^2\omega^2)+a_3b(3\omega^2-b^2)+a_2(b^2-\omega^2)-a_1b+a_0]$ $Q=[4b\omega(\omega^2-b^2)+a_3\omega(3b^2-\omega^2)-a_22b\omega+a_1\omega]$ $\phi_1=\tan^{-1}\left[\dfrac{c^4-a_2c^2+a_0}{c(a_1-a_3c^2)}\right]+\tan^{-1}\left(\dfrac{c}{d}\right)+\tan^{-1}\left(\dfrac{2bc}{b^2+\omega^2-c^2}\right)$ $\phi_2=\tan^{-1}\left(\dfrac{R}{Q}\right)+\tan^{-1}\left(\dfrac{\omega}{d-b}\right)-\tan^{-1}\left(\dfrac{2b\omega}{b^2-\omega^2+c^2}\right)$

NO.	F(s)	f(t)
466	$\frac{s^4+a_3s^3+a_2s^2+a_1s+a_o}{s[(s+b)^2+\omega^2]^2}$	$\frac{a_o}{(b^2+\omega^2)^2}+\frac{1}{2\omega^2}\sqrt{\frac{R^2+Q^2}{(b^2+\omega^2)}}\,t\epsilon^{-bt}\cos(\omega t+\phi_1)+\frac{1}{2\omega^3(b^2+\omega^2)}\sqrt{T^2+X^2}\,\epsilon^{-bt}\cos(\omega t+\phi_2)$ $R=\left[(b^4+\omega^4-6b^2\omega^2)+a_3b(3\omega^2-b^2)+a_2(b^2-\omega^2)-a_1b+a_o\right]$ $Q=\left[4b\omega(\omega^2-b^2)+a_3\omega(3b^2-\omega^2)-a_2 2b\omega+a_1\omega\right]$ $T=\left[b(7\omega^4-2b^2\omega^2-b^4)+a_3(b^4-\omega^4)+a_2b(\omega^2-b^2)+a_1(b^2-\omega^2)-a_ob\right]$ $X=2\omega\left[(b^4+4b^2\omega^2-\omega^4)-a_3b(\omega^2+b^2)+a_2b^2-a_1b+a_o\right]$ $\phi_1=\tan^{-1}\left(\frac{Q}{R}\right)+\tan^{-1}\left(\frac{\omega}{b}\right),\ \phi_2=2\tan^{-1}\left(\frac{\omega}{b}\right)-\tan^{-1}\left(\frac{T}{X}\right)$
467	$\frac{s^4+a_3s^3+a_2s^2+a_1s+a_o}{(s+c)[(s+b)^2+\omega^2]^2}$	$\frac{c^4-a_3c^3+a_2c^2-a_1c+a_o}{[(b-c)^2+\omega^2]^2}\epsilon^{-ct}-\frac{1}{2\omega^2}\sqrt{\frac{R^2+Q^2}{(c-b)^2+\omega^2}}\,t\epsilon^{-bt}\cos(\omega t+\phi_1)$ $+\frac{1}{2\omega^3[(c-b)^2+\omega^2]}\sqrt{T^2+X^2}\,\epsilon^{-bt}\cos(\omega t+\phi_2)$ $R=\left[(b^4+\omega^4-6b^2\omega^2)+a_3b(3\omega^2-b^2)+a_2(b^2-\omega^2)-a_1b+a_o\right]$ $Q=\left[4b\omega(\omega^2-b^2)+a_3\omega(3b^2-\omega^2)-a_2 2b\omega+a_1\omega\right]$ $T=2\omega\left[(b^4+4b^2\omega^2-4b\omega^2c-\omega^4)-a_3(b\omega^2+b^3-\omega^2c)+a_2b^2-a_1b+a_o\right]$ $X=\left[(b^5-b^4c+2b^3\omega^2-6b^2\omega^2c-7b\omega^4+3\omega^4c)+a_3(\omega^4-b^4+b^3c+3b\omega^2c)\right.$ $\left.+a_2(b^3-b\omega^2-b^2c-\omega^2c)+a_1(\omega^2-b^2+bc)+a_o(b-c)\right]$ $\phi_1=\tan^{-1}\left(\frac{Q}{R}\right)-\tan^{-1}\left(\frac{\omega}{c-b}\right),\ \phi_2=\tan^{-1}\left(\frac{X}{T}\right)-2\tan^{-1}\left(\frac{\omega}{c-b}\right)$
468	$\frac{s^4+a_3s^3+a_2s^2+a_1s+a_o}{s[(s+b)^2+\omega^2][(s+c)^2+d^2]}$	$\frac{a_o}{(b^2+\omega^2)(c^2+d^2)}-\frac{1}{\omega}\sqrt{\frac{R^2+Q^2}{(b^2+\omega^2)\{[(c-b)^2+\omega^2-d^2]^2+4d^2(c-b)^2\}}}\,\epsilon^{-bt}\cos(\omega t+\phi_1)$ $-\frac{1}{d}\sqrt{\frac{T^2+X^2}{(c^2+d^2)\{[(c-b)^2+\omega^2-d^2]^2+4d^2(c-b)^2\}}}\,\epsilon^{-ct}\cos(dt+\phi_2)$ $R=\left[(b^4+\omega^4-6b^2\omega^2)+a_3b(3\omega^2-b^2)+a_2(b^2-\omega^2)-a_1b+a_o\right]$ $Q=\left[4b\omega(\omega^2-b^2)+a_3\omega(3b^2-\omega^2)-a_2 2b\omega+a_1\omega\right]$ $T=\left[(c^4+d^4-6c^2d^2)+a_3c(3d^2-c^2)+a_2(c^2-d^2)-a_1c+a_o\right]$ $X=\left[4cd(d^2-c^2)+a_3d(3c^2-d^2)-a_2 2cd+a_1d\right]$ $\phi_1=\tan^{-1}\left(\frac{Q}{R}\right)-\tan^{-1}\left(\frac{b}{\omega}\right)-\tan^{-1}\left[\frac{2\omega(c-b)}{(c-b)^2-\omega^2+d^2}\right]$ $\phi_2=\tan^{-1}\left(\frac{X}{T}\right)-\tan^{-1}\left(\frac{c}{d}\right)-\tan^{-1}\left[\frac{2d(b-c)}{(c-b)^2+\omega^2-d^2}\right]$

NO.	F(s)	f(t)
469	$\dfrac{s^4+a_3s^3+a_2s^2+a_1s+a_0}{(s+f)\left[(s+b)^2+\omega^2\right]\left[(s+c)^2+d^2\right]}$	$\dfrac{f^4-a_3f^3+a_2f^2-a_1f+a_0}{\left[(b-f)^2+\omega^2\right]\left[(c-f)^2+d^2\right]}\epsilon^{-ft}$ $+\dfrac{1}{\omega}\sqrt{\dfrac{R^2+Q^2}{\left[(f-b)^2+\omega^2\right]\left\{\left[(c-b)^2+\omega^2-d^2\right]^2+4d^2(c-b)^2\right\}}}\epsilon^{-bt}\cos(\omega t-\phi_1)$ $+\dfrac{1}{d}\sqrt{\dfrac{T^2+X^2}{\left[(f-c)^2+d^2\right]\left\{\left[(c-b)^2+\omega^2-d^2\right]^2+4d^2(c-b)^2\right\}}}\epsilon^{-ct}\cos(dt-\phi_2)$ $R=\left[(b^4+\omega^4-6b^2\omega^2)+a_3b(3\omega^2-b^2)+a_2(b^2-\omega^2)-a_1b+a_0\right]$ $Q=\left[4b\omega(\omega^2-b^2)+a_3\omega(3b^2-\omega^2)-a_22b\omega+a_1\omega\right]$ $T=\left[(c^4+d^4-6c^2d^2)+a_3c(3d^2-c^2)+a_2(c^2-d^2)-a_1c+a_0\right]$ $X=\left[4cd(d^2-c^2)+a_3d(3c^2-d^2)-a_22cd+a_1d\right]$ $\phi_1=\tan^{-1}\left(\dfrac{R}{Q}\right)+\tan^{-1}\left(\dfrac{\omega}{f-b}\right)+\tan^{-1}\left[\dfrac{2\omega(c-b)}{(c-b)^2-\omega^2+d^2}\right]$ $\phi_2=\tan^{-1}\left(\dfrac{T}{X}\right)+\tan^{-1}\left(\dfrac{d}{f-c}\right)+\tan^{-1}\left[\dfrac{2d(b-c)}{(c-b)^2+\omega^2-d^2}\right]$
470	$\dfrac{1}{s\sinh(as)}$	$2\sum_{k=0}^{\infty}u_{-1}\left[t-(2k+1)a\right]$ 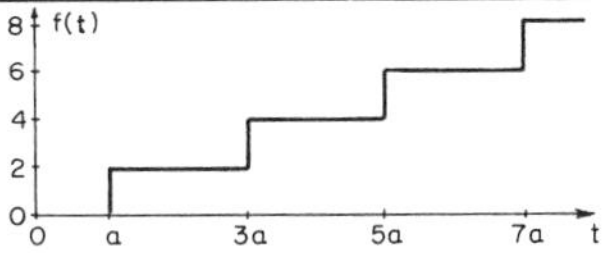
471	$\dfrac{1}{s\cosh s}$	$2\sum_{k=0}^{\infty}(-1)^k u_{-1}(t-2k-1)$ 
472	$\dfrac{1}{s}\tanh\left(\dfrac{as}{2}\right)$	$u_{-1}(t)+2\sum_{k=1}^{\infty}(-1)^k u_{-1}(t-ak)$ SQUARE WAVE 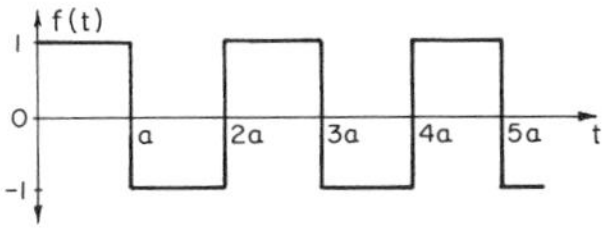
473	$\dfrac{1}{2s}\left(1+\coth\dfrac{as}{2}\right)$	$\sum_{k=\sigma}^{\infty}u_{-1}(t-ka)$ STEPPED FUNCTION 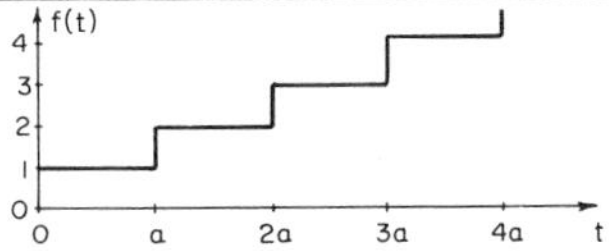
474	$\dfrac{m}{s^2}-\dfrac{ma}{2s}\left(\coth\dfrac{as}{2}-1\right)$	$mt-ma\sum_{k=1}^{\infty}u_{-1}(t-ka)$ SAW-TOOTH FUNCTION 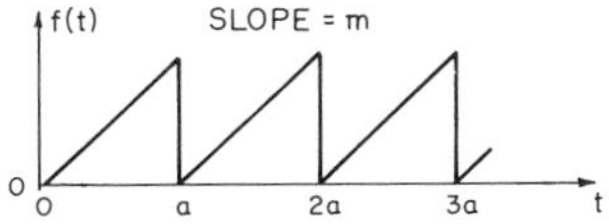

NO.	F(s)	f(t)
475	$\frac{1}{s^2}\tanh\frac{as}{2}$	$\frac{1}{a}\left[t+2\sum_{k=1}^{\infty}(-1)^k(t-ka)\cdot U_{-1}(t-ka)\right]$ TRIANGULAR WAVE 
476	$\frac{1}{s(1+\epsilon^{-s})}$	$\sum_{k=0}^{\infty}(-1)^k\cdot U_{-1}(t-k)$ 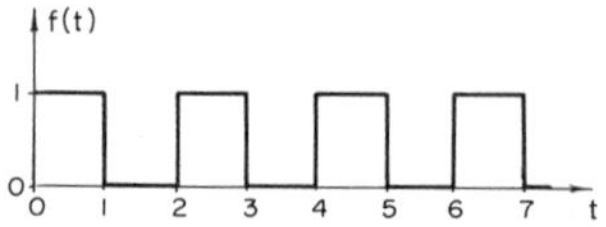
477	$\frac{a}{(s^2+a^2)(1-\epsilon^{-\frac{\pi}{a}s})}$	$\sum_{k=0}^{\infty}\left[\sin a(t-k\frac{\pi}{a})\right]\cdot U_{-1}(t-k\frac{\pi}{a})$ HALF-WAVE RECTIFICATION OF SINE WAVE 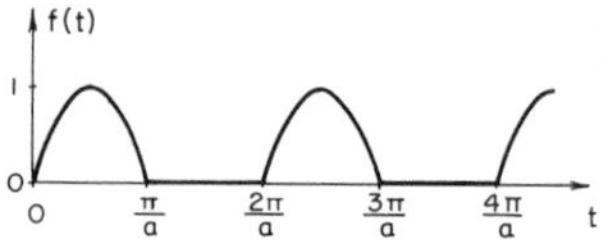
478	$\left[\frac{a}{s^2+a^2}\right]\coth\left(\frac{\pi s}{2a}\right)$	$\left[\sin(at)\right]\cdot U_{-1}(t)+2\sum_{k=1}^{\infty}\left[\sin a(t-k\frac{\pi}{a})\right]\cdot U_{-1}(t-k\frac{\pi}{a})$ FULL-WAVE RECTIFICATION OF SINE WAVE 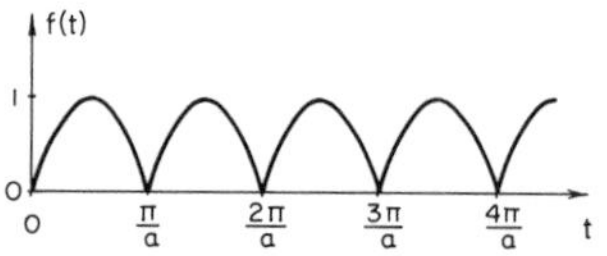
479	$\frac{1}{s}\epsilon^{-as}$	$U_{-1}(t-a)$ 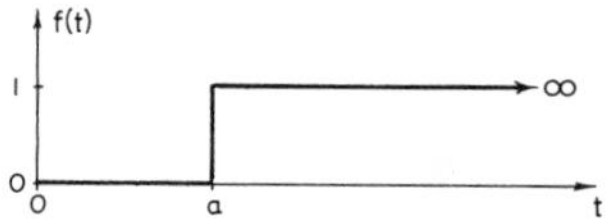
480	$\frac{1}{s}(\epsilon^{-as}-\epsilon^{-bs})$	$U_{-1}(t-a)-U_{-1}(t-b)$ 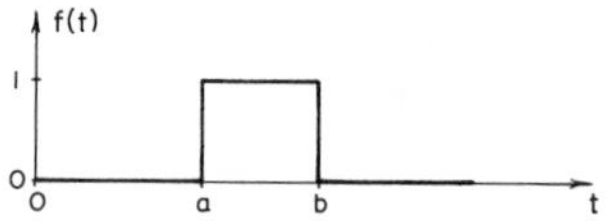
481	$\frac{m}{s^2}\epsilon^{-as}$	$m\cdot(t-a)\cdot U_{-1}(t-a)$ 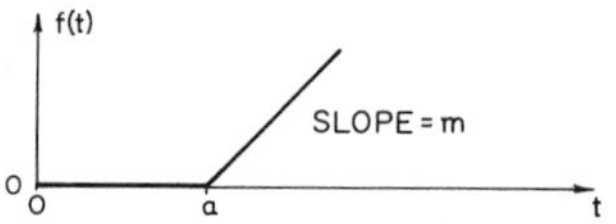
482	$\left[\frac{E}{s}+\frac{m}{s^2}\right]\epsilon^{-as}$	$mt\cdot U_{-1}(t-a)$ or $\left[E+m(t-a)\right]\cdot U_{-1}(t-a)$ where $E=ma$ 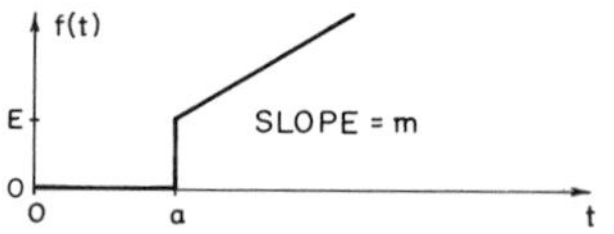
483	$\frac{2}{s^3}\epsilon^{-as}$	$(t-a)^2\cdot U_{-1}(t-a)$ 

NO.	F(s)	f(t)
484	$\left[\frac{2}{s^3}+\frac{2a}{s^2}+\frac{a^2}{s}\right]\epsilon^{-as}$	$t^2 \cdot U_{-1}(t-a)$ 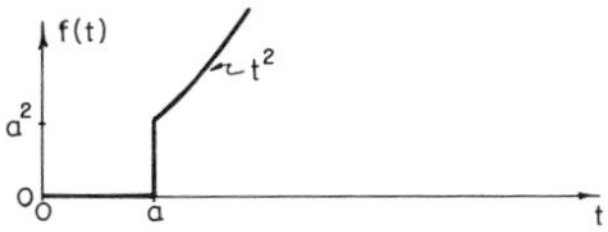
485	$\frac{m}{s^2}-\frac{m}{s^2}\epsilon^{-as}$	$mt \cdot U_{-1}(t) - m(t-a) \cdot U_{-1}(t-a)$ 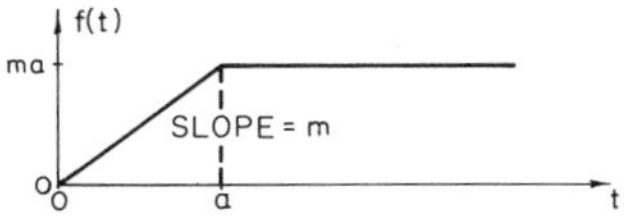
486	$\frac{m}{s^2}-\frac{2m}{s^2}\epsilon^{-as}+\frac{m}{s^2}\epsilon^{-2as}$	$mt-2m(t-a) \cdot U_{-1}(t-a)+m(t-2a) \cdot U_{-1}(t-2a)$ 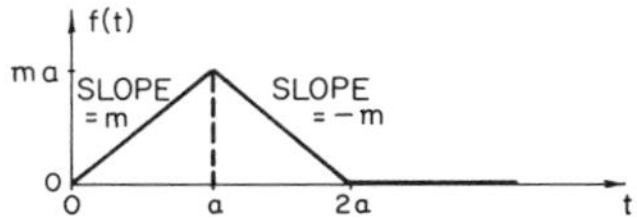
487	$\frac{m}{s^2}-\left(\frac{ma}{s}+\frac{m}{s^2}\right)\epsilon^{-as}$	$mt-\left[ma+m(t-a)\right] \cdot U_{-1}(t-a)$ 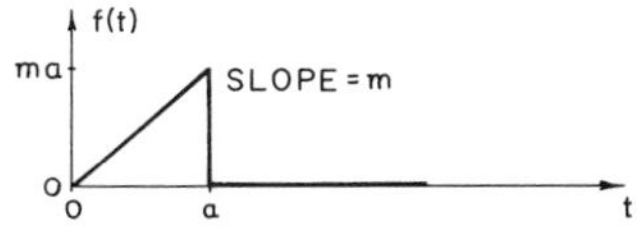
488	$\frac{(1-\epsilon^{-s})^2}{s^3}$	$0.5t^2$ for $0 \leq t < 1$ $1-0.5(t-2)^2$ for $1 \leq t < 2$ 1 for $2 \leq t$ 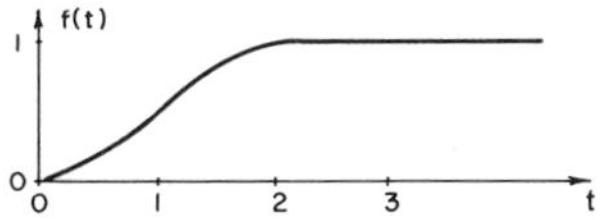
489	$\left[\frac{(1-\epsilon^{-s})}{s}\right]^3$	$0.5t^2$ for $0 \leq t < 1$ $0.75-(t-1.5)^2$ for $1 \leq t < 2$ $0.5(t-3)^2$ for $2 \leq t < 3$ 0 for $3 < t$ 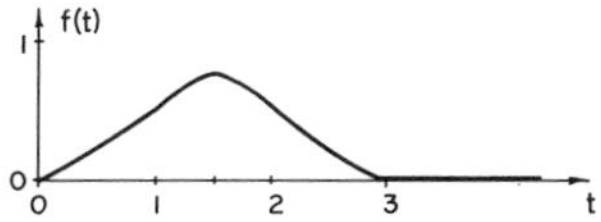
490	$\frac{b}{s(s-b)}+(\epsilon^{ba}-1)\left[\frac{1}{s+b}-\frac{s+\frac{b}{\epsilon^{ba}-1}}{s(s-b)}\right]\epsilon^{-as}$	$(\epsilon^{bt}-1) \cdot U_{-1}(t)-(\epsilon^{bt}-1) \cdot U_{-1}(t-a)+K\epsilon^{-b(t-a)} \cdot U_{-1}(t-a)$ where $K=(\epsilon^{ba}-1)$ 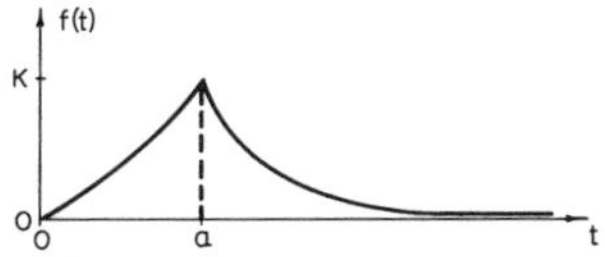

NO.	F(s)	f(t)
491	$\tan^{-1}\left(\frac{a}{s}\right)$	$\frac{1}{t}\sin at$
492	$\frac{1}{s}\tan^{-1}\left(\frac{a}{s}\right)$	si(at) si is the sine integral function. $si(x)=\int_0^1 \frac{\sin x\omega}{\omega}d\omega$
493	$\tan^{-1}\left(\frac{a}{s-b}\right)$	$\epsilon^{bt}\frac{\sin at}{t}$
494	$\ln\left(\frac{s+b}{s+a}\right)$	$\frac{1}{t}(\epsilon^{-at}-\epsilon^{-bt})$
495	$\ln\left(\frac{s+a}{s-a}\right)$	$\frac{2}{t}\sinh at \quad Re[s]>Re[a]$
496	$\ln\sqrt{1+\frac{4a^2}{s^2}}$	$\frac{2}{t}\sin^2 at$
497	$\ln\sqrt{1-\frac{4a^2}{s^2}}$	$-\frac{2}{t}\sinh^2 at$
498	$\frac{1}{s}\ln(s^2+a^2) \quad a>0$	$2\ln a-2ci(at)$, ci is the cosine integral function. $ci(x)=-\int_1^\infty \frac{\cos x\omega}{\omega}d\omega$
499	$\frac{1}{s}\ln s$	$-0.5772-\ln t$
500	$\frac{\ln s}{s^2+1}$	$si(t)\cos t-ci(t)\sin t$ where si is the sine integral function, $si(x)=\int_0^1 \frac{\sin x\omega}{\omega}d\omega$; ci is the cosine integral function, $ci(x)=-\int_1^\infty \frac{\cos x\omega}{\omega}d\omega$
501	$\frac{s\ln s}{s^2+1}$	$-si(t)\sin t-ci(t)\cos t$ where si is the sine integral function, $si(x)=\int_0^1 \frac{\sin x\omega}{\omega}d\omega$; ci is the cosine integral function, $ci(x)=-\int_1^\infty \frac{\cos x\omega}{\omega}d\omega$
502	$\ln\left(\frac{s^2+a^2}{s^2}\right)$	$\frac{2}{t}(1-\cos at)$
503	$\ln\left(\frac{s^2-a^2}{s^2}\right)$	$\frac{2}{t}(1-\cosh at)$
504	$\epsilon^{-as}-\epsilon^{-a\sqrt{s^2+b^2}}$	$\frac{ab}{\sqrt{t^2-a^2}}J_1\left(b\sqrt{t^2-a^2}\right)\cdot u_{-1}(t-a)$ J_1 is Bessel function of 1st kind, 1st order.
505	$\epsilon^{-a\sqrt{s^2-b^2}}-\epsilon^{-as}$	$\frac{ab}{\sqrt{t^2-a^2}}I_1\left(b\sqrt{t^2-a^2}\right)\cdot u_{-1}(t-a)$ I_1 is modified Bessel function of 1st kind, 1st order.
506	$\epsilon^{-a\sqrt{s}} \quad a>0$	$\frac{a}{2\sqrt{\pi t^3}}\epsilon^{-\frac{a^2}{4t}}$

NO.	F(s)	f(t)
507	$s^{-\frac{1}{2}}\epsilon^{-a\sqrt{s}}$ $a>0$	$\frac{1}{\sqrt{\pi t}}\epsilon^{-\frac{a^2}{4t}}$
508	$\frac{1}{s}\epsilon^{-a\sqrt{s}}$ $a\geq 0$	$\text{erfc}\left(\frac{a}{2\sqrt{t}}\right)=1-\text{erf}\left(\frac{a}{2\sqrt{t}}\right)$, erf(y) is the error function. $\text{erf}(y)=\frac{2}{\sqrt{\pi}}\int_0^y \epsilon^{-\omega^2}d\omega$
509	$\frac{\epsilon^{-a\sqrt{s}}}{s+b\sqrt{s}}$ $a>0$	$\epsilon^{b^2t+ab}\left[1-\text{erf}\left(b\sqrt{t}+\frac{a}{2\sqrt{t}}\right)\right]$, erf(y) is the error function. $\text{erf}(y)=\frac{2}{\sqrt{\pi}}\int_0^y \epsilon^{-\omega^2}d\omega$
510	$\frac{1}{s}\epsilon^{-\frac{a}{s}}$	$J_0(2\sqrt{at})$ J_0 is Bessel function of 1st kind, zero order.
511	$\frac{\sqrt{\pi}\,\epsilon^{-\frac{a}{4(s+b)}}}{\sqrt{s+b}}$	$\frac{1}{\sqrt{t}}\epsilon^{-bt}\cos\sqrt{at}$
512	$s^{-\frac{3}{2}}\epsilon^{-\frac{a}{s}}$	$\frac{1}{\sqrt{\pi a}}\sin(2\sqrt{at})$
513	$s^{-\frac{3}{2}}\epsilon^{\frac{a}{s}}$	$\frac{1}{\sqrt{\pi a}}\sinh(2\sqrt{at})$
514	$s^{-\frac{1}{2}}\epsilon^{-\frac{a}{s}}$	$\frac{1}{\sqrt{\pi t}}\cos(2\sqrt{at})$
515	$s^{-\frac{1}{2}}\epsilon^{\frac{a}{s}}$	$\frac{1}{\sqrt{\pi t}}\cosh(2\sqrt{at})$
516	$s^{-(n+1)}\epsilon^{-\frac{1}{s}}$ $Re[n]>-1$	$t^{\frac{n}{2}}J_n(2\sqrt{t})$, J_n is Bessel function of 1st kind, nth order.
517	$\epsilon^{\frac{s^2}{4a}}\text{erfc}\left(\frac{s}{2\sqrt{a}}\right)$ $\text{erfc}(y)=1-\text{erf}(y)$ $\text{erf}(y)=\frac{2}{\sqrt{\pi}}\int_0^y\epsilon^{-\omega^2}d\omega$	$2\sqrt{\frac{a}{\pi}}\,\epsilon^{-at^2}$
518	$\frac{\epsilon^{-\frac{x}{v}\sqrt{(s+a)^2-b^2}}}{\sqrt{(s+a)^2-b^2}}$	0 for $t<\frac{x}{v}$ $\epsilon^{-at}I_0\left(b\sqrt{t^2-\frac{x^2}{v^2}}\right)$ for $t\geq\frac{x}{v}$, I_0 is modified Bessel function of 1st kind, zero order.
519	$\frac{\epsilon^{-a\sqrt{s^2+b^2}}}{\sqrt{s^2+b^2}}$ $a>0$	0 for $0<t<a$ $J_0(b\sqrt{t^2-a^2})$ for $t\geq a$, J_0 is Bessel function of 1st kind, zero order.
520	$\frac{1}{\sqrt{s^2-b^2}}\epsilon^{-a\sqrt{s^2-b^2}}$ $a>0$	0 for $0<t<a$ $I_0(b\sqrt{t^2-a^2})$ for $t\geq a$, I_0 is modified Bessel function of 1st kind, zero order.

CHAPTER 2

Theorems Associated With the Laplace Transform

2-1 Theorem 1 The Laplace Transform

If f(t) is a real function and is defined and single valued almost everywhere for $t \geqq 0$, with t a real variable, and is such that the integral

$$\int_0^{\infty} |f(t)| e^{-\sigma t}\, dt \qquad (\sigma = \text{some real number}) \tag{2-1}$$

converges, then f(t) will be called Laplace transformable, and

$$\mathcal{L}\left[f(t)\right] = F(s) = \int_0^{\infty} f(t) e^{-st} dt \tag{2-2}$$

Example 2-1

$$\mathcal{L}\left[e^{-at}\right] = \int_0^{\infty} e^{-at} e^{-st} dt = \frac{-1}{s + a} \cdot e^{-(s+a)t} \Big|_0^{\infty} = \frac{1}{s + a} . \tag{2-3}$$

2-2 Theorem 2 The Inverse Laplace Transform

If F(s) is the Laplace transform of f(t) and σ_a, the abscissa of convergence, is less than c, then

$$\mathcal{L}^{-1}\left[F(s)\right] = f(t) = \frac{1}{2\pi j} \int_{c-j\infty}^{c+j\infty} F(s) e^{st} ds \tag{2-4}$$

The specified contour of integration must enclose all the poles of F(s).

Example 2-2

Determine the inverse transform of $F(s) = \frac{1}{s(s + a)}$. The integral expression of (2-4) may be evaluated as the sum of the residues of $F(s) \cdot e^{st}$ with respect to all of the poles of F(s).

$$\mathcal{L}^{-1}\left[\frac{1}{s(s + a)}\right] = f(t) = s\left[\frac{e^{st}}{s(s + a)}\right]_{s=0} + (s + a)\left[\frac{e^{st}}{s(s + a)}\right]_{s=-a} \qquad 2\text{-}5$$

$$= \frac{1}{a} - \frac{e^{-at}}{a} = \frac{1}{a}(1 - e^{-at}). \qquad 2\text{-}6$$

2-3 Theorem 3 Linearity (1)

If the functions $f_1(t)$ and $f_2(t)$ are Laplace transformable and have transforms $F_1(s)$ and $F_2(s)$, respectively, then

$$\mathcal{L}\left[f_1(t) \pm f_2(t)\right] = F_1(s) \pm F_2(s). \qquad 2\text{-}7$$

Example 2-3

$$\mathcal{L}\left[e^{-at} + \sin\omega t\right] = \frac{1}{s + a} + \frac{\omega}{s^2 + \omega^2} \qquad 2\text{-}8$$

2-4 Theorem 4 Linearity (2)

If f(t) has the Laplace transform F(s), and K is a constant or a variable which is independent of t and s, then

$$\mathcal{L}\left[K \cdot f(t)\right] = K \cdot F(s). \qquad 2\text{-}9$$

Example 2-4

$$\mathcal{L}\left[5 \cdot te^{-at}\right] = \frac{5}{(s + a)^2} \qquad 2\text{-}10$$

2-5 Theorem 5 Real Differentiation

If the function f(t) and its derivative $\frac{d\,f(t)}{dt}$ are Laplace transformable, and the transform of f(t) is F(s), then

$$\mathcal{L}\left[\frac{d\,f(t)}{dt}\right] = s \cdot F(s) - f(0^-) \qquad 2\text{-}11$$

where $f(0^-)$ is the initial value of f(t) at $t = 0^-$.

For the nth derivative of f(t),

$$\mathcal{L}\left[\frac{d^n f(t)}{dt^n}\right] = s^n \cdot F(s) - \sum_{\ell=1}^{n} s^{(\ell-1)} \cdot f^{(n-\ell)}(0^-) \qquad 2\text{-}12$$

where $f^{(n-\ell)}(0^-)$ is the initial value of the $(n-\ell)^{th}$ derivative of f(t) at $t = 0^-$. If any g(t) is continuous at t = 0, then $g(0^+)$ can be used as well as $g(0^-)$. However, if a discontinuity exists at t = 0, then $g(0^-)$ should be used.

Example 2-5

The displacement of a certain mass is x(t) feet with an initial value of 5 feet. The initial velocity, x'(0), is 27 feet/second, and the initial acceleration, x''(0), is 93 feet/(sec)^2. Then,

$$\mathcal{L}\left[\frac{d^3x(t)}{dt^3}\right] = s^3 \cdot X(s) - x''(0^-) - s \cdot x'(0^-) - s^2 \cdot x(0^-) \qquad 2\text{-}13$$

$$= s^3 \cdot X(s) - 93 - s(27) - s^2(5). \qquad 2\text{-}14$$

2-6 Theorem 6 Real Integration

If the function f(t) is Laplace transformable and has the transform F(s), then its integral

$$\int f(t)dt = \int_0^t f(t)dt + f^{-1}(0^+) \qquad 2\text{-}15$$

has the transform

$$\mathcal{L}\left[\int f(t)dt\right] = \frac{F(s)}{s} + \frac{f^{-1}(0^+)}{s} \qquad 2\text{-}16$$

where $f^{-1}(0^+)$ is the initial value of the integral of $f(t)$ at $t = 0^+$.

Example 2-6

The velocity of a certain mass is $v(t)$, and the initial displacement is 5. Then,

$$\mathcal{L}\left[\int v(t)dt\right] = \frac{V(s)}{s} + \frac{5}{s}\,. \qquad 2\text{-}17$$

2-7 Theorem 7 Multiplication by s

If $f(t)$ and its derivative, $f'(t)$, are Laplace transformable, and $F(s)$ is the transform of $f(t)$, and if $f(0^+) = 0$, then

$$s \cdot F(s) = \mathcal{L}\left[f'(t)\right]. \qquad 2\text{-}18$$

Multiplication by s in the complex s domain corresponds to differentiation in the real t domain.

Example 2-7

$$s\left[\frac{b - a}{(s + a)(s + b)}\right] = \mathcal{L}\left[\frac{d}{dt}(e^{-at} - e^{-bt})\right]. \qquad 2\text{-}19$$

2-8 Theorem 8 Division by s

If $F(s)$ is the Laplace transform of $f(t)$, then

$$\frac{F(s)}{s} = \mathcal{L}\left[\int_0^t f(t)dt\right]. \qquad 2\text{-}20$$

Division by s in the complex s domain corresponds to definite integration in the real t domain.

Example 2-8

$$\frac{1}{s}\left[\frac{sb}{s^2 + b^2}\right] = \mathcal{L}\left[\int_0^t b \cdot \cos(bt)dt\right] . \qquad 2\text{-}21$$

2-9 Theorem 9 Scale Change

If F(s) is the Laplace transform of f(t), and a is a positive constant, or a second positive variable which is independent of t and s, then,

$$\mathcal{L}\left[f(\tfrac{t}{a})\right] = a \cdot F(as). \qquad 2\text{-}22$$

Example 2-9

If $f(t) = e^{-bt}$, and $f(s) = \frac{1}{s + b}$, then

$$\mathcal{L}\left[e^{\frac{-bt}{a}}\right] = \frac{a}{as + b} = \frac{1}{s + \frac{b}{a}} . \qquad 2\text{-}23$$

2-10 Theorem 10 Complex Multiplication (Real Convolution)

If F(s) and G(s) are the Laplace transforms of f(t) and g(t), respectively, then

$$\mathcal{L}\left[\int_0^t f(t - x) \cdot g(x)dx\right] = F(s) \cdot G(s). \qquad 2\text{-}24$$

Example 2-10

Find the inverse transform of $\frac{1}{s(s + a)}$. Let $F(s) = \frac{1}{s + a}$, and $G(s) = \frac{1}{s}$. Then, $f(t) = e^{-at}$, and $g(t) = U_{-1}(t)$.

Now, $$\mathcal{L}^{-1}\left[F(s)\cdot G(s)\right] = \int_0^t e^{-a(t-x)}\cdot U_{-1}(x)dx \qquad 2\text{-}25$$

$$= e^{-at}\int_0^t e^{ax}dx = \frac{e^{-at}}{a}\left[e^{ax}\right]_{x=0}^{t} = \frac{1}{a}(1-e^{-at}) \ . \qquad 2\text{-}26$$

2-11 <u>Theorem 11</u> Real Multiplication (Complex Convolution)

If $F_1(s)$ and $F_2(s)$ are the Laplace transforms of $f_1(t)$ and $f_2(t)$, respectively, then

$$\mathcal{L}\left[f_1(t)\cdot f_2(t)\right] = \frac{1}{2\pi j}\int_{c-j\infty}^{c+j\infty} F_1(P)\cdot F_2(s-P)dP \qquad 2\text{-}27$$

where max $(\sigma_{a1}, \sigma_{a2}, \sigma_{a1}+\sigma_{a2}) < \sigma$, and $\sigma_{a2} < c < \sigma - \sigma_{a1}$

and where c is a real constant; $\sigma = \mathrm{Re}[s]$; σ_{a1} and σ_{a2} are the abscissas of absolute convergence of $f_1(t)$ and $f_2(t)$, respectively.

(a) When $F_1(s)$ is rational function, $F_1(s) = \frac{A_1(s)}{B_1(s)}$, and has only q first-order poles, then

$$\mathcal{L}\left[f_1(t)\cdot f_2(t)\right] = \sum_{k=1}^{q} \frac{A_1(s_k)}{B_1'(s_k)}\cdot F_2(s-s_k) \qquad 2\text{-}28$$

where the s_k are the poles of $F_1(s)$.

<u>Example 2-11a</u>

Determine the transform for $f_1(t)\cdot f_2(t)$, where

$$f_1(t) = \frac{1}{a}(1-e^{-at}) \quad ; \quad F_1(s) = \frac{1}{s(s+a)}$$

and $$f_2(t) = bt \quad ; \quad F_2(s) = \frac{b}{s^2} \ .$$

Then, $\mathcal{L}\left[f_1(t)f_2(t)\right] = \left[\frac{1}{2s + a}\right]_{s=0} \cdot \left[\frac{b}{(s - P)^2}\right]_{P=0} + \left[\frac{1}{2s + a}\right]_{s=-a} \cdot \left[\frac{b}{(s - P)^2}\right]_{P=-a}$ 2-29

$$= \frac{b}{as^2} - \frac{b}{a}\left[\frac{1}{(s + a)^2}\right] = \frac{b}{a}\left[\frac{1}{s^2} - \frac{1}{(s + a)^2}\right] . \qquad 2\text{-}30$$

(b) When $F_1(s)$ is a rational function having n poles and where the pole, s_k, has an order of m_k, then

$$\mathcal{L}\left[f_1(t) \cdot f_2(t)\right] = \sum_{k=1}^{n} \sum_{j=1}^{m_k} \frac{(-1)^{m_k - j} \cdot K_{kj}}{(m_k - j)!} \left[\frac{d^{m_k - j}}{ds^{m_k - j}} F_2(s)\right]_{s=s-s_k} \qquad 2\text{-}31$$

where

$$K_{kj} = \frac{1}{(j-1)!}\left[\frac{d^{j-1}}{ds^{j-1}} (s - s_k)^{m_k} \cdot F_1(s)\right]_{s=s_k} . \qquad 2\text{-}32$$

<u>Example 2-11b</u>

Determine the transform of $f_1(t) \cdot f_2(t)$, where

$$f_1(t) = 1 - e^{-at} - ate^{-at} \quad ; \quad F_1(s) = \frac{a}{s(s + a)^2}$$

and

$$f_2(t) = U_{-1}(t) \quad ; \quad F_2(s) = \frac{1}{s} .$$

$F_1(s)$ has two poles, $s_1 = 0$ of order 1, and $s_2 = -a$ of order 2.

$$K_{11} = \left.\frac{a}{(s + a)^2}\right|_{s=0} = \frac{1}{a} \qquad 2\text{-}33$$

$$K_{21} = \left.\frac{a}{s}\right|_{s=-a} = -1 \qquad 2\text{-}34$$

$$K_{22} = \frac{d}{ds}\left[\frac{a}{s}\right]_{s=-a} = -\frac{1}{a} . \qquad 2\text{-}35$$

$$\mathcal{L}\left[f_1(t)\cdot f_2(t)\right] = \frac{1}{a}\left[\frac{1}{s}\right]_{s=s-0} + \frac{d}{ds}\left[\frac{1}{s}\right]_{s=s+a} - \frac{1}{a}\left[\frac{1}{s}\right]_{s=s+a} \qquad 2\text{-}36$$

$$= \frac{1}{as} - \frac{1}{(s+a)^2} - \frac{1}{a(s+a)} \;. \qquad 2\text{-}37$$

2-12 Theorem 12 Real Translation

If f(t) has the Laplace transform, F(s), and if a is a non-negative real number, then

(a) $\mathcal{L}[f(t-a)] = e^{-as}\cdot F(s)$ where $f(t-a) = 0$, $0 < t < a$. 2-38

(b) $\mathcal{L}[f(t+a)] = e^{as}\cdot F(s)$ where $f(t+a) = 0$, $-a < t < 0$. 2-39

Example 2-12

If $f(t) = e^{-bt}$ is shifted in time to become

$$f(t-a) = e^{-b(t-a)}\cdot U_{-1}(t-a), \text{ then} \qquad 2\text{-}40$$

$$\mathcal{L}\left[e^{-b(t-a)}U_{-1}(t-a)\right] = e^{-as}\cdot\frac{1}{s+b} \;. \qquad 2\text{-}41$$

2-13 Theorem 13 Complex Translation

If f(t) has the Laplace transform F(s) and if P is a complex number with non-negative real part, then

(a) $\mathcal{L}\left[e^{-Pt}\cdot f(t)\right] = F(s+P)$. 2-42

(b) $\mathcal{L}\left[e^{Pt}\cdot f(t)\right] = F(s-P)$. 2-43

Example 2-13

$$\mathcal{L}\left[e^{-(a+j\omega)t}\cdot e^{-bt}\right] = \frac{1}{(s+a+j\omega)+b} = \frac{1}{s+a+b+j\omega} \;. \qquad 2\text{-}44$$

2-14 Theorem 14 Second Independent Variable

Let a be a second variable that is independent of t as well as s. If f(t,a) has the transform F(s,a), with respect to t, and $\lim_{a \to a_0} [f(t,a)]$ and $\lim_{a \to a_0} [F(s,a)]$ exist, then

$$\mathcal{L}_t\left[\lim_{a \to a_0} f(t,a)\right] = \lim_{a \to a_0} F(s,a). \qquad 2\text{-}45$$

The interpretation of this theorem is that the limit process with respect to a is invariant under the transformation from the real domain to the complex domain.

Example 2-14

$$\mathcal{L}_t\left[\lim_{a \to 0}(e^{-at} + e^{-bt})\right] = \lim_{a \to 0}\left[\frac{1}{s+a} + \frac{1}{s+b}\right] = \frac{1}{s} + \frac{1}{s+b}\,. \qquad 2\text{-}46$$

2-15 Theorem 15 Differentiation With Respect to a Second Independent Variable

Let a be a second variable that is independent of t as well as s. If f(t,a) has the transform F(s,a), with respect to t, and if $\frac{\partial}{\partial a} f(t,a)$ exists, then

$$\mathcal{L}_t\left[\frac{\partial}{\partial a} f(t,a)\right] = \frac{\partial}{\partial a} F(s,a). \qquad 2\text{-}47$$

Example 2-15

$$\mathcal{L}_t\left[\frac{\partial}{\partial a}(1 - e^{-at})\right] = \frac{\partial}{\partial a}\left[\frac{1}{s} - \frac{1}{s+a}\right] = \frac{1}{(s+a)^2} \qquad 2\text{-}48$$

2-16 Theorem 16 Final Value

If f(t) and f'(t) are Laplace transformable, and $\mathcal{L}[f(t)]$ is F(s), and the function $s \cdot F(s)$ has no poles on the imaginary axis and in the right half-plane, then

$$\lim_{t \to \infty} f(t) = \lim_{s \to 0} s \cdot F(s). \qquad 2\text{-}49$$

<u>Example 2-16</u>

What is the final value of the time function, $f(t)$, whose transform is

$$F(s) = \frac{K(s+a)}{s(s+b)(s+c)^2} . \qquad 2\text{-}50$$

$$f(\infty) = \lim_{t \to \infty} f(t) = \lim_{s \to 0} s \cdot \frac{K(s+a)}{s(s+b)(s+c)^2} = \frac{Ka}{bc^2} . \qquad 2\text{-}51$$

2-17 <u>Theorem 17</u> Initial Value

If $f(t)$ and $f'(t)$ are Laplace transformable and $\mathcal{L}[f(t)]$ is $F(s)$, and the limit $\lim_{s \to \infty} s \cdot F(s)$ exists, then

$$\lim_{t \to 0} f(t) = \lim_{s \to \infty} s \cdot F(s). \qquad 2\text{-}52$$

<u>Example 2-17</u>

What is the initial value of the time function, $f(t)$, whose transform is

$$F(s) = \frac{Ks}{(s+a)^2} . \qquad 2\text{-}53$$

$$f(0^+) = \lim_{t \to 0} f(t) = \lim_{s \to \infty} s \cdot \frac{Ks}{(s+a)^2} = K . \qquad 2\text{-}54$$

2-18 <u>Theorem 18</u> Complex Differentiation

If $\mathcal{L}[f(t)]$ is $F(s)$, then

$$\mathcal{L}[t \cdot f(t)] = -\frac{d}{ds} F(s) \qquad 2\text{-}55$$

Example 2-18

If $f(t) = e^{-at}$, then

$$\mathcal{L}\left[t \cdot e^{-at}\right] = - \frac{d}{ds}\left[\frac{1}{s+a}\right] = \frac{1}{(s+a)^2} \ . \qquad \text{2-56}$$

2-19 Theorem 19 Complex Integration

If f(t) and f(t)/t are Laplace transformable, and $\mathcal{L}$[f(t)] is F(s), and if $\int_s^\infty F(s)ds$ exists, then

$$\mathcal{L}\left[\frac{f(t)}{t}\right] = \int_s^\infty F(s)\ ds \ . \qquad \text{2-57}$$

Example 2-19

Determine the transform of

$$g(t) = \frac{\sin(\omega t)}{\omega t} \ . \qquad \text{2-58}$$

Let $f(t) = [\sin(\omega t)]/\omega$. Therefore, $\mathcal{L}[f(t)] = 1/(s^2 + \omega^2)$.

Then

$$\mathcal{L}[g(t)] = \int_s^\infty \frac{1}{s^2 + \omega^2}\ ds = \frac{1}{\omega} \cdot \tan(\frac{s}{\omega}) \Big|_s^\infty = \frac{1}{\omega}\left[\frac{\pi}{2} - \tan^{-1}(\frac{s}{\omega})\right] \qquad \text{2-59}$$

$$= \frac{1}{\omega} \tan^{-1}(\frac{\omega}{s}). \qquad \text{2-60}$$

2-20 Theorem 20 Integration With Respect to a Second Independent Variable

If a is a second variable that is independent of t as well as s, and $\mathcal{L}$[f(t,a)] with respect to t is F(s,a), and if the integrals involved exist, then

$$\mathcal{L}\left[\int_{ao}^{a} f(t,a)da\right] = \int_{ao}^{a} F(s,a)da. \quad 2\text{-}61$$

Example 2-20

Determine the transform of

$$g(t) = \frac{\sin(\omega t)}{t}. \quad 2\text{-}62$$

Recognizing that $\int_0^{\omega} \cos(\omega t)d\omega$ is $[\sin(\omega t)]/t$, let $f(t,\omega) = \cos(\omega t)$, then

$$\mathcal{L}[g(t)] = \mathcal{L}_t\left[\int_0^{\omega} \cos(\omega t)d\omega\right] = \int_0^{\omega} \frac{s}{(s^2+\omega^2)}\, d\omega \quad 2\text{-}63$$

$$= \tan^{-1}\left(\frac{\omega}{s}\right)\Bigg|_0^{\omega} = \tan^{-1}\left(\frac{\omega}{s}\right). \quad 2\text{-}64$$

2-21 Theorem 21 Commutativity of Laplace Transform With Real and Imaginary Transformations

If f(t) is complex and has the transform F(s), then

(a) $\mathcal{L}[\text{Re } f(t)] = \text{Re}\mathcal{L}[f(t)] = \text{Re } F(s)$ 2-65

(b) $\mathcal{L}[\text{Im } f(t)] = \text{Im}\mathcal{L}[f(t)] = \text{Im } F(s).$ 2-66

Example 2-21

$$\mathcal{L}\left\{\text{Re}\left[e^{j\omega t}\right]\right\} = \text{Re}\mathcal{L}\left[e^{j\omega t}\right] = \text{Re}\left[\frac{1}{s-j\omega}\right] = \frac{s}{s^2+\omega^2}. \quad 2\text{-}67$$

CHAPTER 3

Functions of a Complex Variable

3-1 Introduction

The study of transient responses of physical systems occupies a prominent place in the training program of the modern engineer. Akin to this area in an inseparable manner is the study of complex functions. The transform equations and transfer functions describing the performance of systems are functions of complex variables.

The objective at hand is to present and review some of the more often encountered properties and theorems related to complex functions and the study of the dynamics of physical systems. In this presentation, mathematical rigor may not always be adhered to in the most strict sense, the emphasis being on a working familiarity with functions of a complex variable.

3-2 The Imaginary Number

Any positive number can be graphically represented as shown in Figure 3-1 as the one-dimensional phasor extending to the right from the reference zero origin to a point representing that number.

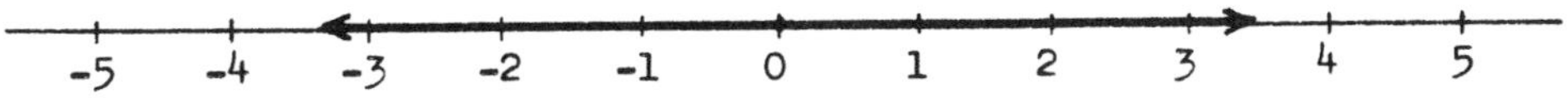

Figure 3-1. The Scale of Real Numbers

Similarly, a negative number can logically be represented by a phasor extending to the left of the same origin. This implies that when a negative sign replaces the positive sign in front of a number, the phasor whose length represents the magnitude of the number, undergoes a rotation of 180 degrees. These positive and negative numbers are said to be <u>real numbers</u>.

Therefore, if -1 is considered to be a unit phasor, rotated 180° from the reference position corresponding to +1, then $\sqrt{-1}$ could be considered to be a unit phasor rotated 90° from the reference position. It follows then,

$$
\begin{aligned}
+1 &= 1 \,\underline{/0^\circ} \\
\sqrt{-1} &= 1 \,\underline{/90^\circ} \\
(\sqrt{-1})^2 &= 1 \,\underline{/180^\circ} \qquad \text{3-1} \\
(\sqrt{-1})^3 &= 1 \,\underline{/270^\circ} \\
(\sqrt{-1})^4 &= 1 \,\underline{/0^\circ}
\end{aligned}
$$

Thus, $\sqrt{-1}$ effectively has a rotating property of 90°, and can be considered to be a rotating operator. For convenience, a special symbol j will be assigned to represent it. Furthermore, $\sqrt{-1}$ is called an imaginary number. It is observed that,

$$
\begin{aligned}
j &= 1 \,\underline{/90^\circ} \\
j^2 &= -1 = 1 \,\underline{/180^\circ} \\
j^3 &= -j = 1 \,\underline{/270^\circ} \qquad \text{3-2} \\
j^4 &= +1 = 1 \,\underline{/0^\circ}
\end{aligned}
$$

So now an imaginary quantity such as $\sqrt{-25}$ becomes

$$\sqrt{-25} = \sqrt{-1} \cdot (5) = j5 = 5 \underline{/90^\circ} \qquad 3\text{-}3$$

and is represented graphically as shown in Figure 3-2. The vertical axis in the figure is usually referred to as the imaginary axis, or the quadrature axis.

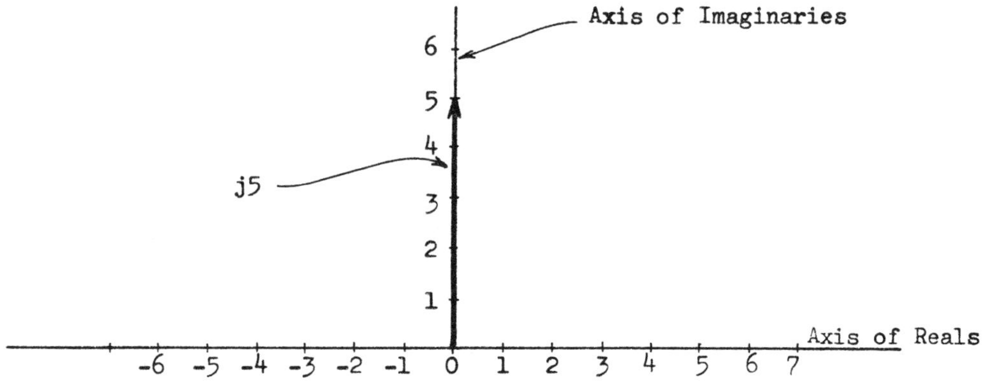

Figure 3-2. The Axis of Imaginaries

3-3 The Complex Number

If some number is given as a "mixture" consisting of one part that is real and another part that is imaginary, then that number is said to be a complex number. Thus, the number, $s = \sigma + j\omega$, is a complex number, and is shown in Figure 3-3 as the sum of the two phasors, σ and $j\omega$. The value of s can be quoted in rectangular form as $\sigma + j\omega$, or in polar form as $r \underline{/\theta}$. The plane upon which s is plotted is called the complex plane, the Argand diagram, or simply, the s-plane.

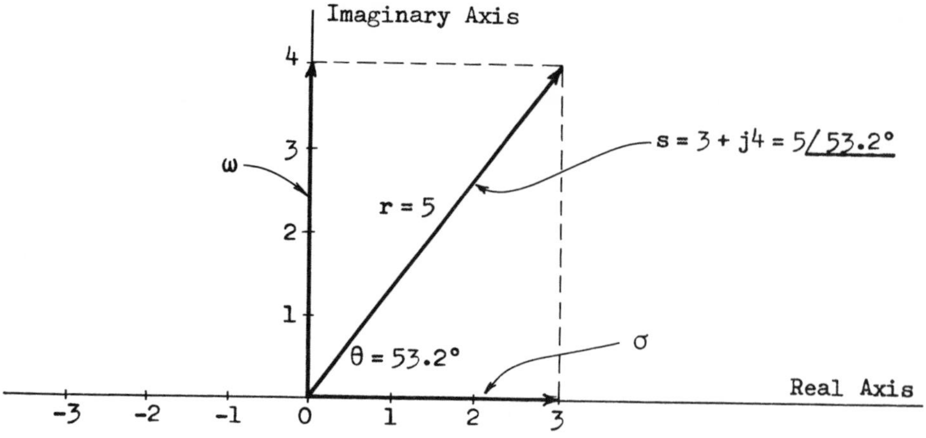

Figure 3-3 Mapping of a Complex Number on the Complex Plane

From the geometry of Figure 3-3, it is seen that

$$r = \sqrt{\sigma^2 + \omega^2} \qquad 3\text{-}4$$

$$\theta = \arctan (\omega/\sigma) \qquad 3\text{-}5$$

$$\sigma = r \cdot \cos \theta \qquad 3\text{-}6$$

$$\omega = r \cdot \sin \theta \qquad 3\text{-}7$$

$$s = \sigma + j\omega = r(\cos \theta + j \cdot \sin \theta) = r \underline{/\theta} = r \cdot e^{j\theta}. \qquad 3\text{-}8$$

3-4 Arithmetic and Miscellaneous Operations

The following definitions and identities are given for reference and are offered without proof.

Addition

$$s_1 + s_2 = (\sigma_1 + j\omega_1) + (\sigma_2 + j\omega_2) = (\sigma_1 + \sigma_2) + j(\omega_1 + \omega_2) \qquad 3\text{-}9$$

Multiplication

$$s_1 \cdot s_2 = (\sigma_1 + j\omega_1) \cdot (\sigma_2 + j\omega_2)$$

$$= (\sigma_1 \sigma_2 - \omega_1\omega_2) + j(\sigma_2 \omega_1 + \sigma_1\omega_2) = r_1 \cdot r_2 \underline{/\theta_1 + \theta_2} . \qquad 3\text{-}10$$

Division

$$\frac{s_1}{s_2} = \frac{(\sigma_1 + j\omega_1)}{(\sigma_2 + j\omega_2)} = \frac{(\sigma_1\sigma_2 + \omega_1\omega_2)}{\sigma_2^2 + \omega_2^2} + \frac{j(\sigma_2\omega_1 - \sigma_1\omega_2)}{\sigma_2^2 + \omega_2^2} = \left[\frac{r_1}{r_2}\right] \angle\theta_1 - \theta_2 .$$

3-11

Miscellaneous

$\bar{s} = \sigma - j\omega$ 3-12

$(\overline{s_1 + s_2}) = \bar{s}_1 + \bar{s}_2$ 3-13

$(\overline{s_1 \cdot s_2}) = \bar{s}_1 \cdot \bar{s}_2$ 3-14

$\overline{\left[\frac{s_1}{s_2}\right]} = \frac{\bar{s}_1}{\bar{s}_2}$ 3-15

$s + \bar{s} = 2 \cdot \mathrm{Re}(s)$ 3-16

$s - \bar{s} = 2 \cdot j \cdot \mathrm{Im}(s)$ 3-17

$s \cdot \bar{s} = |s|^2$ 3-18

$|s_1 + s_2| \leq |s_1| + |s_2|$ 3-19

$|s_2 - s_1| \geq |s_2| - |s_1|$ 3-20

$s^n = r^n(\cos(n\theta) + j\sin(n\theta)) = r^n \angle n\theta$ (For integer n, positive or negative)

3-21

$\sqrt[n]{s} = \sqrt[n]{r} \angle \frac{\theta + 2k\pi}{n}$ (k = 0, 1, 2, ..., n-1) 3-22

3-5 Complex Functions

If $g = f(s)$, where $s = \sigma + j\omega$, then $f(s)$ is said to be a function of a complex variable. It follows then, that g must be complex; that is, $g = u + jv$. Thus, $u = \mathrm{Re}\, f(s)$ and $v = \mathrm{Im}\, f(s)$.

Consider $s = \sigma + j\omega$ to be the complex number represented by any point in the s-plane (σ, ω plane).

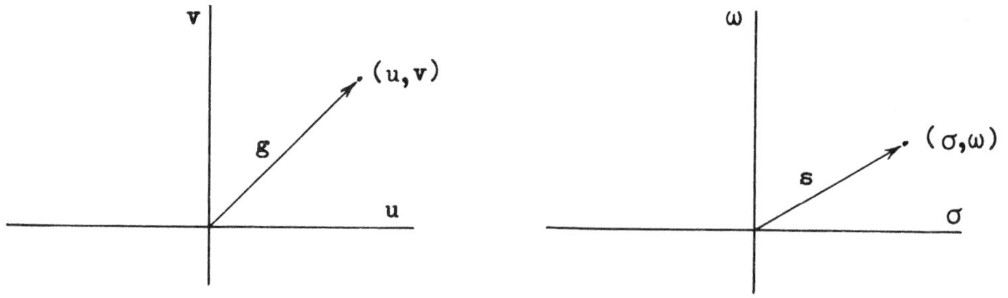

(a) The g-plane (b) The s-plane

Figure 3-4

Now, if g = f(s), and if g is related to s in a way such that for every value of s in a region R, there is one and only one corresponding value of g, then g is said to be a single-valued function of s. Examples of single-valued functions are

$$g_1 = s, \quad g_2 = \frac{1}{s}, \quad g_3 = \frac{1}{1 + 3s}, \quad g_4 = \frac{40(s + 2)}{s(s + 4)(s + 6)}. \tag{3-23}$$

Consider the foregoing function g_4 for a moment. It is seen that it is not defined everywhere in the s-plane. Specifically, it is not defined at s = 0, -4, and -6. These points are poles of the function. It is further noted that the function goes to zero at s = -2. This point is called a zero of the function. In contrast to the foregoing single-valued functions is a classic example of a multiple-valued function; namely,

$$g = \sqrt{s}. \tag{3-24}$$

3-6 Examples of Complex Functions of Varied Forms

Polynomial: $g = a_o s^n + a_1 s^{n-1} + \dots + a_{n-1} s + a_n$ 3-25

Rational Function: $$g = \frac{a_o s^n + \dots + a_n}{b_o s^m + \dots + b_m}$$ 3-26

Exponential: $g = e^s$ 3-27

Logarithm: $g = \log(s)$ 3-28

Power: $g = s^a$ 3-29

Trigonometric: $$g = \sin(s) = \frac{e^{js} - e^{-js}}{2j}$$ 3-30

Hyperbolic: $$g = \cos h(s) = \frac{e^s - e^{-s}}{2}$$ 3-31

Inverse Trigonometric: $g = \text{arc}\sin(s)$. 3-32

Example 3-1

Determine $u(\sigma, \omega)$ and $v(\sigma, \omega)$ for $g = \frac{10}{s + 2}$.

Substituting $\sigma + j\omega$ for s,

$$g = \frac{10}{\sigma + j\omega + 2} = \frac{10(\sigma + 2 - j\omega)}{(\sigma + 2 + j\omega)(\sigma + 2 - j\omega)}$$ 3-33

$$= \frac{10(\sigma + 2)}{(\sigma + 2)^2 + \omega^2} - j\frac{10\omega}{(\sigma + 2)^2 + \omega^2} .$$ 3-34

Thus,

$$u = \frac{10(\sigma + 2)}{(\sigma + 2)^2 + \omega^2} \quad \text{and}$$ 3-35

$$v = \frac{-10\omega}{(\sigma + 2)^2 + \omega^2}$$ 3-36

3-7 Mapping of Complex Functions

For the real function, $y = f(x)$, y and x, respectively, are one-dimensional and if x, for instance, is allowed to vary, there is only one path it can follow. This depicted in Figure 3-5. The limits on x would be the only necessary specification.

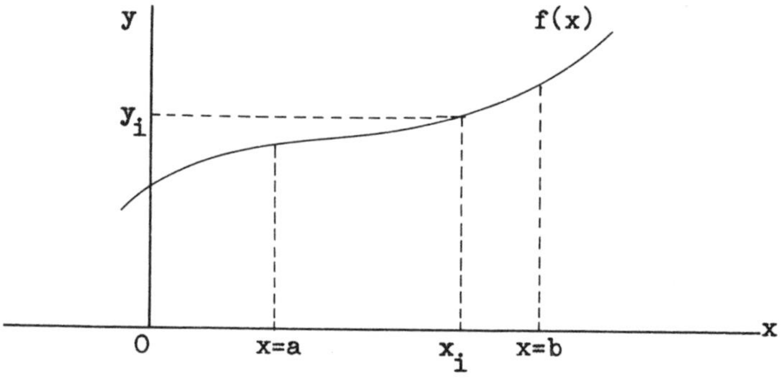

Figure 3-5. Mapping of a Real Function, $y = f(x)$, on the Real Plane

For the cases of complex functions, however, there are four variable quantities; the real and imaginary parts of both the independent variable and the dependent variable. Therefore, when the independent variable s is allowed to vary, there are an infinite number of paths that it can take.

For a given function, $g = f(s)$, the values that g specifically takes on will be determined by what path s is allowed to take. A common way of showing the mapping of g as s is allowed to follow some prescribed path in the s plane is illustrated in the following example. The mapping is shown in Figure 3-6.

Example 3-2

For the transformation,

$$g(s) = \frac{10}{s-2} \tag{3-37}$$

plot the resulting values of g(s) as s is allowed to vary along the specified contour (ABCDEFGHIJKL) as shown in Figure 3-6a.

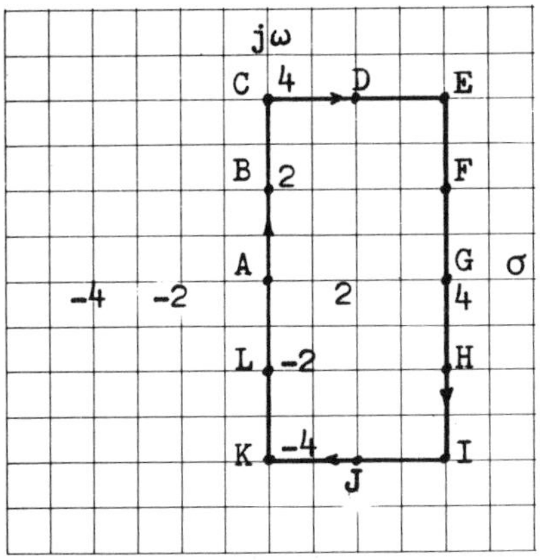

Specified Contour Shown in the s-plane

(a)

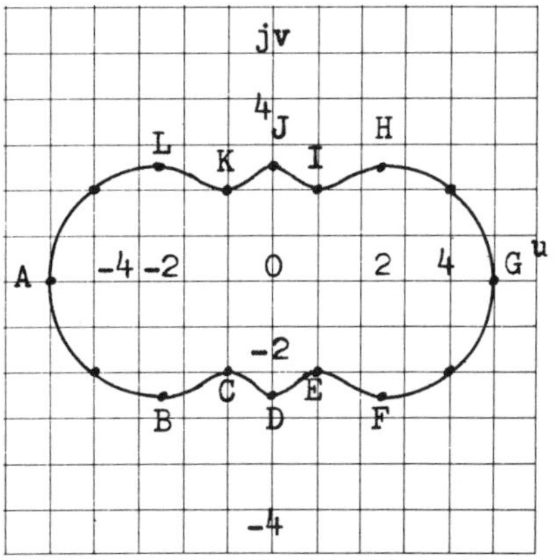

Corresponding Values of g(s) Plotted in the g-plane

(b)

Figure 3-6. Mapping of the Function of Example 3-2

Table 3-1

Tabulated Data for the Function, $g(s) = \frac{10}{s-2}$

Point	s	g(s)
A	0 + j0	-5 + j0
B	0 + j2	-2.5 - j2.5
C	0 + j4	-1 - j2
D	2 + j4	0 - j2.5
E	4 + j4	1 - j2
F	4 + j2	2.5 - j2.5
G	4 + j0	5 + j0
H	4 - j2	2.5 + j2.5
I	4 - j4	1 + j2
J	2 - j4	0 + j2.5
K	0 - j4	-1 + j2
L	0 - j2	-2.5 + j2.5

As the value of s varies along the specified contour shown in Figure 3-6a, the corresponding values of g(s) trace the path presented in Figure 3-6b. Attention is directed to the fact that the path of g(s) encircles the origin on the g-plane in a counterclockwise direction. This will occur when the path of s on the s-plane encircles a single pole of g(s) in a clockwise direction. In Figure 3-6a, the path of s is seen to encircle the point, s = +2, which is a pole of the given function, g(s) = 10/(s-2).

Similarly, it can be shown that when a function g(s) has a zero and the clockwise contour of s encloses only the zero, then the path of g(s) will encircle the origin on the g-plane in a clockwise direction. From this, one might correctly deduce that if the s contour encircled both a zero and a pole of a given function, then the corresponding path of g(s) would not encircle the origin. Furthermore, if the s contour does not encircle either a pole or a zero, then the g(s) contour will not encircle the g-plane origin.

Figure 3-7 shows the mapping of the function of Example 3-2 for the case of an s contour that does not encircle the pole of the function.

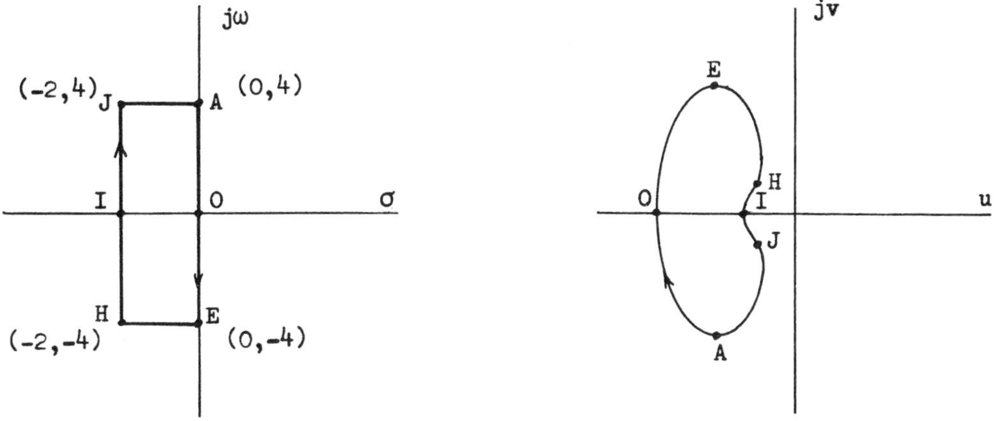

(a) Specified Contour Shown in the s-plane

(b) Corresponding Values of g(s) Plotted in the g-plane

Figure 3-7. Mapping of the Function of Example 3-2

The s-plane contour most commonly specified in association with studies of control systems is along the jω axis and encircling the right half of the s-plane at an infinite radius. The origin is not included within the closed contour but is encircled to the right at an infinitesimal radius. Figure 3-8a illustrates this contour.

Example 3-3

Map the function, $$g(s) = \frac{8}{(s + 2)(s + 10)} \qquad 3\text{-}38$$

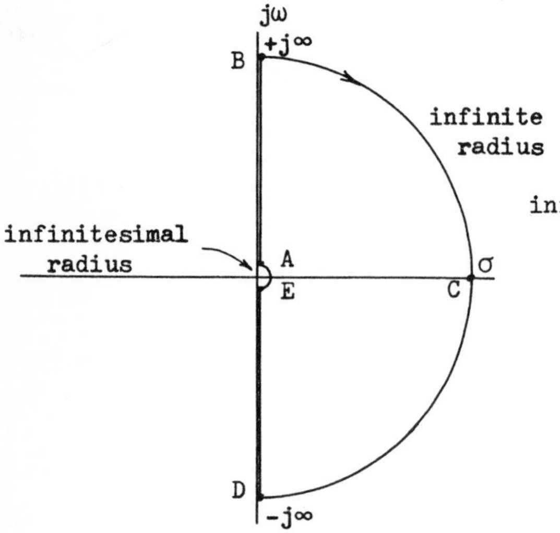

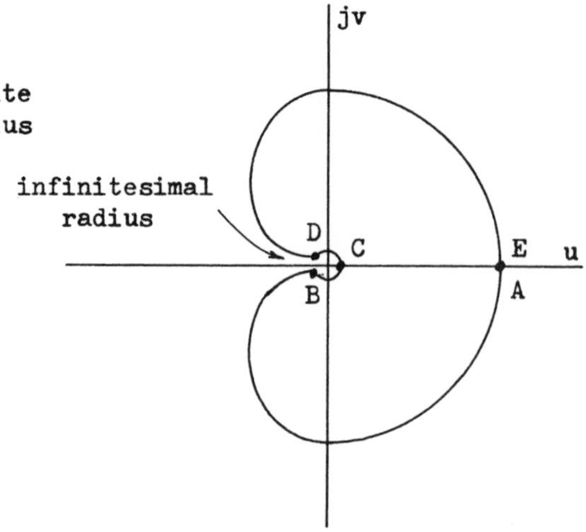

(a) Specified Contour in the s-plane

(b) Corresponding g(s) Plotted in the g-plane (not to scale)

Figure 3-8. Mapping of the Function of Example 3-3

In Example 3-3, note that the s contour does not enclose either of the poles, $s = -2$, $s = -10$, with the result that the g contour does not enclose the origin in the g-plane.

<u>Example 3-4</u>

Map the function, $g(s) = \dfrac{20}{s(s + 2)(s + 10)}$ 3-39

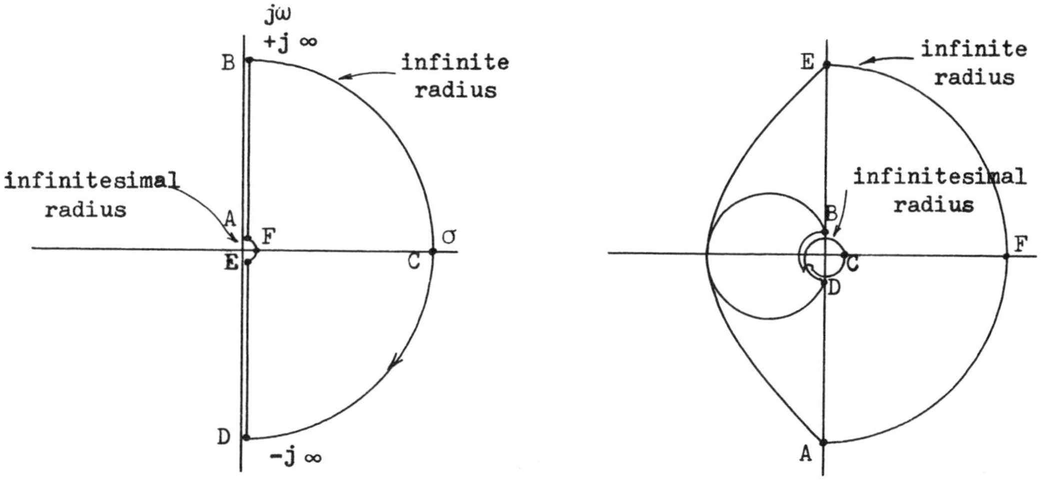

(a) Specified Contour in the s-plane

(b) Corresponding g(s) Plotted in the g-plane (not to scale)

Figure 3-9. Mapping of the Function of Example 3-4

3-8 Singular Points, Regularity, and Analyticity

If the derivative exists for a function at some point $s = s_o$ and in the neighborhood of s_o in the s-plane, then the function is said to be regular at the point.[1] Those functions which have at least one regular point are called analytic functions. A point at which a function is not regular is called a singular point, or a singularity.

A value of s which causes a function to become infinite is always a singularity. In Eq. (3-37), the function becomes infinite for s = +2 and, more specifically, s = +2 is called a pole.

[1]Some authors use the terms regular and analytic interchangeably.

Other types of singularities exist for which a function does not become infinite. The singularities usually encountered in control system studies are poles. Therefore, the following sections will not have much to say about the other types. For the record, however, the classification of singularities in general includes poles, essential singularities, branch points, algebraic singularities, and logarithmic singularities.

If a function F(s) has a singularity at $s = \alpha$, the singularity will be a pole if a positive integer n can be found such that

$$\lim_{s \to \alpha} (s - \alpha)^n \cdot F(s) \tag{3-40}$$

has a nonzero finite value. If such a limit exists, the pole will be of order n. If no such limit exists, then α is an essential singularity. An essential singularity can be viewed as a pole of infinite order.

The classification of single-valued complex functions in terms of their singularities is displayed in Table 3-2.

Table 3-2. Classification of Single-Valued Complex Functions

	Analytic	Meromorphic	Rational	Entire
Finite-plane singularities	Any number, poles or essential	Any number, poles only	Finite number, poles only	None
Singularity at infinity	Pole or essential	Pole or essential	Pole only	Pole or essential

Functions encountered in the studies of control systems are, by far in the majority, rational functions.

3-9 Real Differentiation

For the sake of comparison, the derivative of a real function is reviewed briefly. For the real function, $y = f(x)$, which is typically represented in Figure 3-10,

$$\frac{dy}{dx} = \lim_{\Delta x \to 0} \frac{\Delta y}{\Delta x} = \lim_{\Delta x \to 0} \frac{f(x + \Delta x) - f(x)}{\Delta x} \qquad 3\text{-}41$$

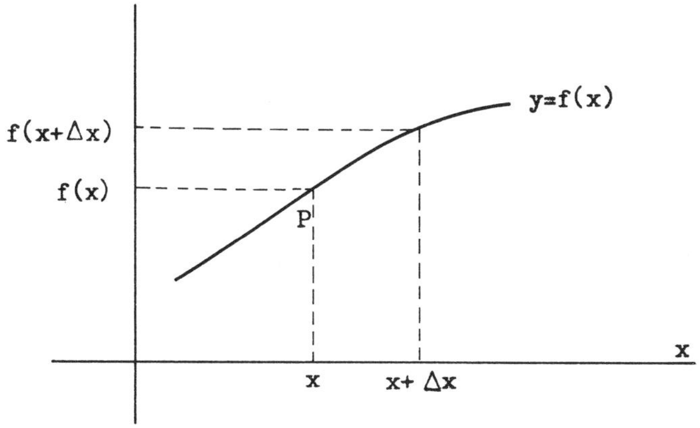

Figure 3-10. The Principle of Real Differentiation

In the case of real differentiation, there is no question as to the manner in which $\Delta x \to 0$ since there is only one path that x can follow.

Example 3-5

Determine $\frac{dy}{dx}$ of the function, $y = 3x^2 + 4$ 3-42

$$\frac{dy}{dx} = \lim_{\Delta x \to 0} \frac{3(x + \Delta x)^2 + 4 - 3x^2 - 4}{\Delta x} \qquad 3\text{-}43$$

$$= \lim_{\Delta x \to 0} \frac{3x^2 + 6x \cdot \Delta x + 3(\Delta x)^2 + 4 - 3x^2 - 4}{\Delta x}$$

$$= \lim_{\Delta x \to 0} (6x + 3 \cdot \Delta x) = 6x \text{ (answer).}$$

3-10 Complex Differentiation

If $g = f(s)$, is a complex function, then the derivative of g with respect to s can be expressed as

$$\frac{dg}{ds} = \lim_{\Delta s \to o} \frac{\Delta g}{\Delta s} = \lim_{\Delta s \to o} \frac{f(s + \Delta s) - f(s)}{\Delta s} \qquad 3\text{-}44$$

where $g = u + jv, \quad \Delta g = \Delta u + j\Delta v$ 3-45

$s = \sigma + j\omega, \quad \Delta s = \Delta\sigma + j\Delta\omega$.

Now, in general, if $f(s) = u(\sigma, \omega) + jv(\sigma, \omega)$ 3-46

then $\lim_{s \to s_1} f(s) = \lim_{\substack{\sigma \to \sigma_1 \\ \omega \to \omega_1}} u + j \cdot \lim_{\substack{\sigma \to \sigma_1 \\ \omega \to \omega_1}} v$ 3-47

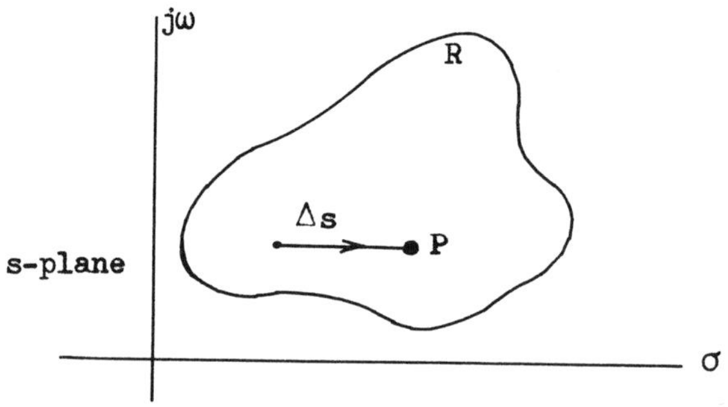

Figure 3-11. One Typical Path for Δs in the Differentiation of a Complex Function

Therefore, if Δs is allowed to approach zero in the σ direction only, as pictured in Figure 3-11, then

$$\frac{dg}{ds} = \lim_{\Delta\sigma \to o} \frac{u(\sigma + \Delta\sigma, \omega) - u(\sigma, \omega)}{\Delta\sigma} + j \cdot \lim_{\Delta\sigma \to o} \frac{v(\sigma + \Delta\sigma, \omega) - v(\sigma, \omega)}{\Delta\sigma} .$$

3-48

The first term in Eq. (3-48) is recognized as $\frac{\partial u}{\partial \sigma}$, and the second as $\frac{\partial v}{\partial \sigma}$, thus

$$\frac{dg}{ds} = \frac{\partial u}{\partial \sigma} + j \frac{\partial v}{\partial \sigma} \qquad 3\text{-}49$$

for Δs in the σ direction. Now, Δs can be allowed to approach zero along an infinite number of paths; the question is then which path should be chosen.

If $g = f(s)$ is analytic in the region R and regular at the point P where the derivative is to be evaluated, then $\frac{dg}{ds}$ will be independent of the direction in which Δs is taken. It is only for analytic functions then that $\frac{dg}{ds}$ really has any meaning. So, for an analytic function, $\frac{dg}{ds}$ can be determined by allowing $\Delta s \to o$ in the ω direction just as well as in the σ direction. Therefore,

$$\frac{dg}{ds} = \lim_{\Delta\omega \to o} \frac{u(\sigma, \omega + \Delta\omega) - u(\sigma, \omega)}{j\Delta\omega} + j \cdot \lim_{\Delta\omega \to o} \frac{v(\sigma, \omega + \Delta\omega) - v(\sigma, \omega)}{j\Delta\omega} \qquad 3\text{-}50$$

$$= -j \frac{\partial u}{\partial \omega} + \frac{\partial v}{\partial \omega} \,. \qquad 3\text{-}51$$

Since Eqs. (3-49) and (3-51) produce the same end result, then it can be said that for analytic functions

$$\frac{\partial u}{\partial \sigma} = \frac{\partial v}{\partial \omega} \text{ and } \frac{\partial v}{\partial \sigma} = -\frac{\partial u}{\partial \omega} \,. \qquad 3\text{-}52$$

These are called the "Cauchy-Riemann" equations and constitute a necessary condition for a function to be analytic. Stated formally,

A necessary and sufficient condition for $f(s) = u(\sigma, \omega) + j \cdot v(\sigma, \omega)$ to be analytic at $s_o = \sigma_o + j \cdot \omega_o$ is that $u(\sigma, \omega)$ and $v(\sigma, \omega)$ together with their partial derivatives be continuous and satisfy the Cauchy-Riemann equations in a neighborhood of (σ_o, ω_o).

The points of the region where f(s) ceases to be analytic are singular points.

Example 3-6

Study the following function for analyticity through the use of the Cauchy-Riemann equations.

$$g = \frac{1}{s} = \frac{1}{\sigma + j\omega} = \frac{\sigma - j\omega}{\sigma^2 + \omega^2} \qquad \text{3-53}$$

$$u = \frac{\sigma}{\sigma^2 + \omega^2} \quad \text{and} \quad v = \frac{-\omega}{\sigma^2 + \omega^2}$$

$$\frac{\partial u}{\partial \sigma} = \frac{-\sigma^2 + \omega^2}{[\sigma^2 + \omega^2]^2} \qquad \text{3-54}$$

$$\frac{\partial v}{\partial \omega} = \frac{-\sigma^2 + \omega^2}{[\sigma^2 + \omega^2]^2} \qquad \text{3-55}$$

$$\frac{\partial v}{\partial \sigma} = \frac{2\sigma\omega}{[\sigma^2 + \omega^2]^2} \qquad \text{3-56}$$

$$-\frac{\partial u}{\partial \omega} = \frac{2\sigma\omega}{[\sigma^2 + \omega^2]^2} . \qquad \text{3-57}$$

It can be seen that the requirements of continuity and the Cauchy-Riemann equations are satisfied everywhere except at s = 0. Thus, the function is analytic everywhere except at the origin. Excluding the origin, the derivative of the function can be expressed as

$$\frac{dg}{ds} = \frac{1}{s^2} = \frac{\partial u}{\partial \sigma} + j \cdot \frac{\partial v}{\partial \sigma} = \frac{-\sigma^2 + \omega^2 + j^2\sigma\omega}{(\sigma^2 + \omega^2)} . \qquad \text{3-58}$$

3-11 Real Integration

The definite integral of a real function is given as

$$\int_{x=a}^{x=b} f(x) \cdot dx = \lim_{\substack{\Delta x \to o \\ n \to \infty}} \sum_{i=1}^{i=n} \overline{f(x)}_i \cdot (\Delta x)_i .$$

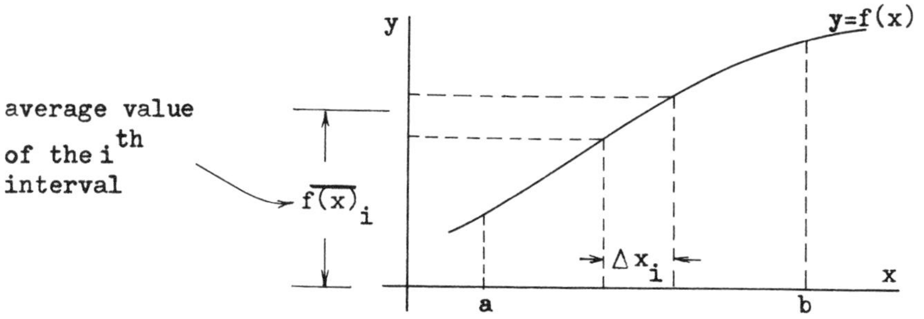

Figure 3-12. Graphical Interpretation of the Real Definite Integral

For the real definite integral, the path of integration can only be along one path and the value of the integral is a function of the end points only. The value of the integral can be interpreted as the area under the curve between the limits of x = a and x = b.

3-12 Complex Integration

The integral of a complex function is written in a manner similar to that of (3-59);

$$\int_{C\ s_1}^{s_2} f(s) \cdot ds = \lim_{\substack{\Delta s \to o \\ n \to \infty}} \sum \overline{f(s)}_i \cdot (\Delta s)_i . \qquad 3\text{-}60$$

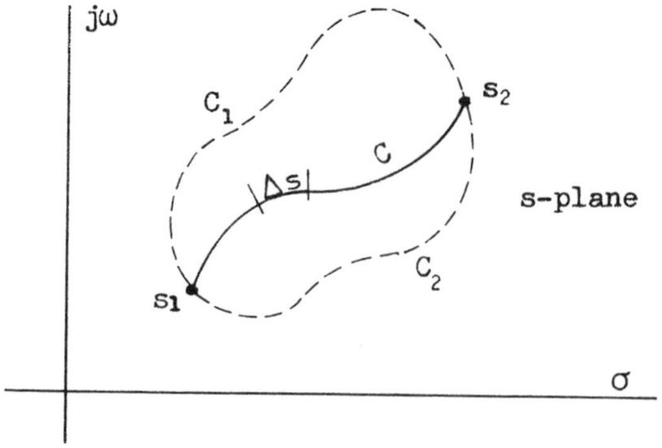

Figure 3-13. Graphical Representation of the Complex Integral

However, since there are an infinite number of paths between the end points, s_1 and s_2, the specific path of integration (contour) must be specified in general and the value of the integral is not necessarily a function of the end points only. The value of the complex integral cannot be interpreted as an area. Replacing s with its components, Eq. (3-60) becomes

$$\int_{C\,s_1}^{s_2} f(s)\cdot ds = \lim_{\substack{n\to\infty \\ \Delta\sigma\to 0 \\ \Delta\omega\to 0}} \sum_{i=1}^{n} (u_i + jv_i)\,(\Delta\sigma + j\Delta\omega) \qquad 3\text{-}61$$

$$= \lim_{\substack{n\to\infty \\ \Delta\sigma\to 0 \\ \Delta\omega\to 0}} \sum_{i=1}^{n} [(u_i\cdot\Delta\sigma_i - v_i\cdot\Delta\omega_i) + j(v_i\cdot\Delta\sigma_i + u_i\cdot\Delta\omega_i)] \qquad 3\text{-}62$$

$$= \int_C (u\cdot d\sigma - v\cdot d\omega) + j\int_C (v\cdot d\sigma + u\cdot d\omega)\,. \qquad 3\text{-}63$$

If the direction of integration along the contour C is reversed, the sign of the integral is reversed. That is,

$$\int_C f(s) \cdot ds = -\int_{-C} f(s) \cdot ds \ . \qquad 3\text{-}64$$

Also, the integration along a specified contour can be performed piecemeal. (Superposition holds)

$$\int_{s_1}^{s_4} f(s) \cdot ds = \int_{s_1}^{s_2} f(s) \cdot ds + \int_{s_2}^{s_3} f(s) \cdot ds + \int_{s_3}^{s_4} f(s) \cdot ds \ . \qquad 3\text{-}65$$

3-13 Integration Around a Closed Path

If it is presumed that

$$\int_{s_1}^{s_2} f(s) \cdot ds \qquad 3\text{-}66$$

is a function of the end points, s_1 and s_2, only, then

$$\int_{s_1}^{s_2} f(s) \cdot ds = \int^{s_2} f(s) \cdot ds - \int^{s_1} f(s) \cdot ds \qquad 3\text{-}67$$

which implies that the value of the integral is independent of the path of integration.

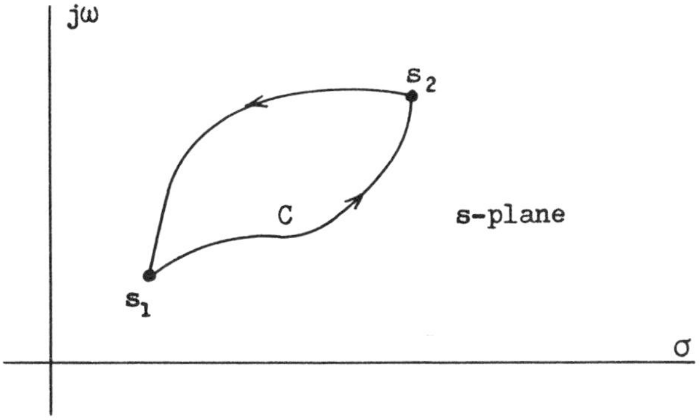

Figure 3-14. A Simple Closed Contour

Then, for a "simple" closed contour as typically shown in Figure 3-14,

$$\oint_C f(s) \cdot ds = \int_{s_1}^{s_2} f(s) \cdot ds + \int_{s_2}^{s_1} f(s) \cdot ds = 0 \qquad 3\text{-}68$$

$$= \oint_C (u \cdot d\sigma - v \cdot d\omega) + j\oint_C (v \cdot d\sigma + u \cdot d\omega) = 0$$

3-69

or

$$\oint_C (u \cdot d\sigma + v \cdot d\omega) = 0, \text{ and } \oint_C (v \cdot d\sigma + u \cdot d\omega) = 0 \,. \qquad 3\text{-}70$$

These last two integrals are functions of the real variables, σ and ω. These integrals will exist if u and v and their derivatives are continuous within and on the contour C. (Analytic)

With respect to the integrals of (3-70), consider, for example, the integral, $\int_C u \cdot d\sigma$. In general, u is a function of both σ and ω; however, in specifying C, ω will be expressed as a function of σ. Thus, u becomes a function of σ only.

Now, consider the following theorem[1] from the theory of real integrals:

> In a simply connected region, R, where the functions M(x,y) and N(x,y) and their partial derivatives are defined and are continuous and single-valued, the integral

$$\oint [M(x,y) \cdot dx + N(x,y) \cdot dy] \qquad 3\text{-}71$$

will vanish if

$$\frac{\partial M}{\partial y} = \frac{\partial N}{\partial x}. \qquad 3\text{-}72$$

---

[1]Sokolnikoff, Advanced Calculus, 1st ed., 1939, p. 185.

Applying the above theorem to (3-70), the result is

$$\frac{\partial u}{\partial \sigma} = \frac{\partial v}{\partial \omega} \text{ and } \frac{\partial u}{\partial \omega} = - \frac{\partial v}{\partial \sigma} . \qquad 3\text{-}73$$

These equations will be recognized as the Cauchy-Riemann equations which, when satisfied, provide one of the conditions necessary for a function to be analytic. The other condition is the above continuity requirement. The conclusion is, therefore, that in order for the value of the integral,

$$\int_{s_1}^{s_2} f(s) \cdot ds$$

to be a function of the end points only, and that

$$\oint_C f(s) \cdot ds = 0,$$

the function must be analytic within and on the contour.

Example 3-6

Consider the function, $g = f(s) = \sigma - j2\omega$. 3-74

Through the application of the Cauchy-Riemann equations, it will be found that the function is nowhere analytic.

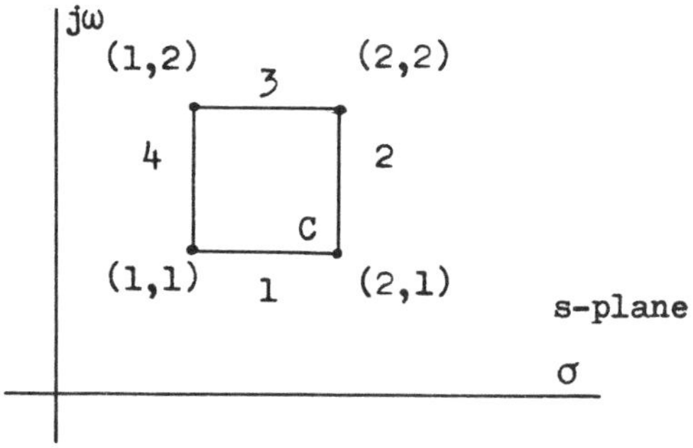

Figure 3-15. The Specified Contour of Integration in Example 3-6

Now, let the closed-contour integral of the given function be evaluated for the contour which is displayed in Figure 3-15. Making use of the form of Eq. (3-69), namely,

$$\oint f(s)\cdot ds = \oint u\,.\,d\sigma + j\oint v\cdot d\sigma - \oint v\cdot d\omega + j\oint u\cdot d\omega \qquad 3\text{-}75$$

and making use of the principle of superposition, the integral of each side of the square contour will be evaluated.

<u>Path 1</u> (σ is variable, $\omega = 1$)

$$\int_{\sigma=1}^{\sigma=2} f(s)\cdot ds = \int_{\sigma=1}^{\sigma=2} \sigma\cdot d\sigma + j\int_{\sigma=1}^{\sigma=2} (-2)(1)\cdot d\sigma - 0 + j0 = 1.5 - j2 \qquad 3\text{-}76$$

<u>Path 2</u> ($\sigma = 2$, ω is variable)

$$\int_{\omega=1}^{\omega=2} f(s)\cdot ds = 0 + j0 - \int_{\omega=1}^{\omega=2} (-2\omega)\cdot d\omega + j\int_{\omega=1}^{\omega=2} 2\cdot d\omega = 3 + j2 \qquad 3\text{-}77$$

<u>Path 3</u> (σ is variable, $\omega = 2$)

$$\int_{\sigma=2}^{\sigma=1} f(s)\cdot ds = \int_{\sigma=2}^{\sigma=1} \sigma\cdot d\sigma + j\int_{\sigma=2}^{\sigma=1} (-2)(2)\cdot d\sigma - 0 + j0 = -1.5 + j4 \qquad 3\text{-}78$$

<u>Path 4</u> ($\sigma = 1$, ω is variable)

$$\int_{\omega=2}^{\omega=1} f(s)\cdot ds = 0 + j0 - \int_{\omega=2}^{\omega=1} (-2\omega)\cdot d\omega + j\int_{\omega=2}^{\omega=1} (1)\cdot d\omega = -3 - j1 \qquad 3\text{-}79$$

Summing the results of the four integrations,

$$\oint_C f(s)\cdot ds = +j3. \qquad 3\text{-}80$$

It was to be expected that the value of the closed-contour integral would not be zero since the given function was not analytic.

3-14 Simply-Connected and Multiply-Connected Regions

A region, R, bounded by the contour, C, is said to be "simply-connected" if the contour can be progressively shrunk to a point without any part of the contour boundary crossing itself. Figure 3-16 depicts a simply-connected region.

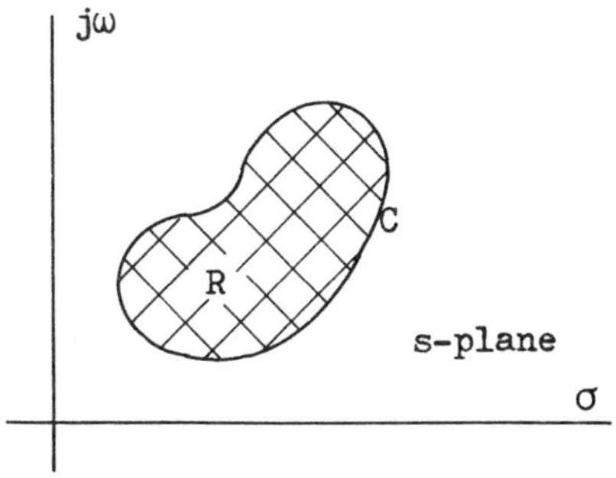

Figure 3-16. A Simply-Connected Region

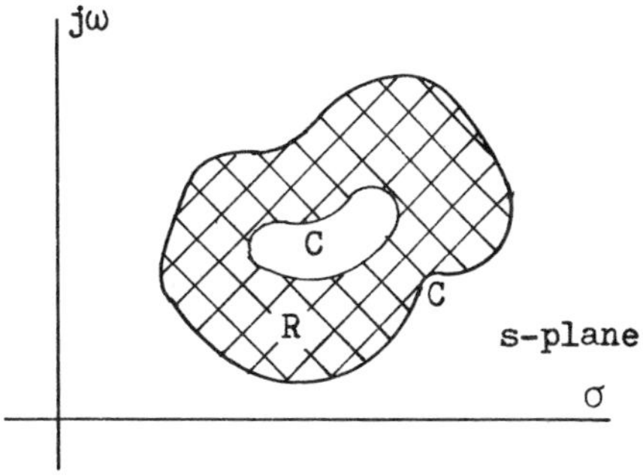

Figure 3-17. A Multiply-Connected Region

A region that does not fulfill the foregoing specifications is illustrated in Figure 3-17. This is referred to as a "multiply-connected" region.

3-15 Complex Integration in a Multiply-Connected Region (Cauchy-Goursat Theorem)

Consider the multiply-connected region shown in Figure 3-18. The given f(s) is analytic in R, and on C, C_1 and C_2, but is not necessarily analytic inside C_1 and C_2, or outside C.

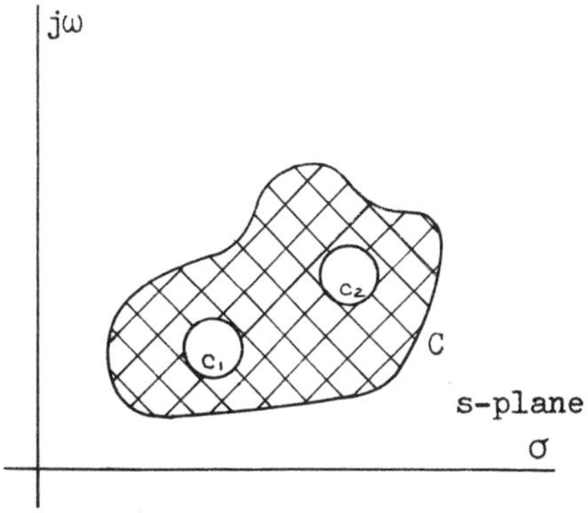

Figure 3-18. Multiply-Connected Region

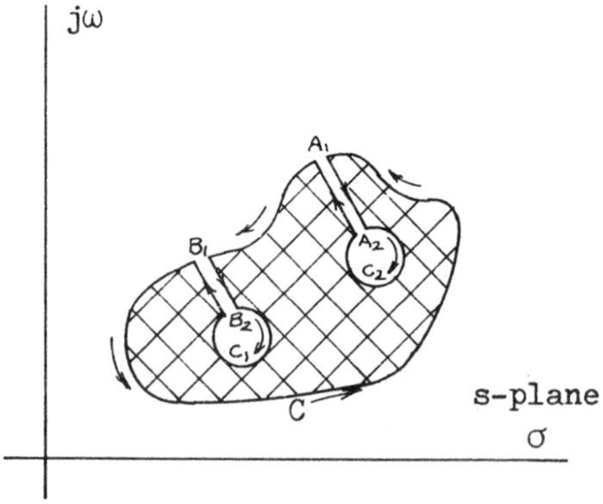

Figure 3-19. Modified Region

Figure 3-19 shows the region modified to the extent of opening infinitesimally small "corridors" into C_1 and C_2. Now, applying known properties of complex integration and due to the fact that the results of integrating along the walls of the "corridors" will cancel,

$$\oint_C f(s) \cdot ds - \oint_{C_1} f(s) \cdot ds - \oint_{C_2} f(s) \cdot ds = 0 \qquad 3\text{-}81$$

since the region bounded is analytic. The contributions of the integrals along the walls of the corridors sum to zero due to the infinitesimal nature of the defined corridors. Note the change in signs of the last two integrals in (3-81) when the directions of C_1 and C_2 were reversed to agree with C. Thus,

$$\oint_C f(s) \cdot ds = \oint_{C_1} f(s) \cdot ds + \oint_{C_2} f(s) \cdot ds \qquad 3\text{-}82$$

One important implication of the foregoing result (3-82), is that when the integral, $\oint_C f(s) \cdot ds$, is to be evaluated around a contour which is known to contain isolated singularities within (the function is not analytic at the singular points, such as poles), then the exact path of the contour, C, is not critical as long as f(s) is analytic along the path. Furthermore, the integral around C can be evaluated by integrating around each singularity within C separately and then summing.

3-16 Cauchy's Integral Formula

In association with Figure 3-20, it is known that h(s) is analytic within C and on C. α is a point within the contour C. Then the function,

$$f(s) = \frac{h(s)}{s - \alpha} \qquad 3\text{-}83$$

is analytic everywhere within and on C, except at point α. α is a singularity (pole) of f(s).

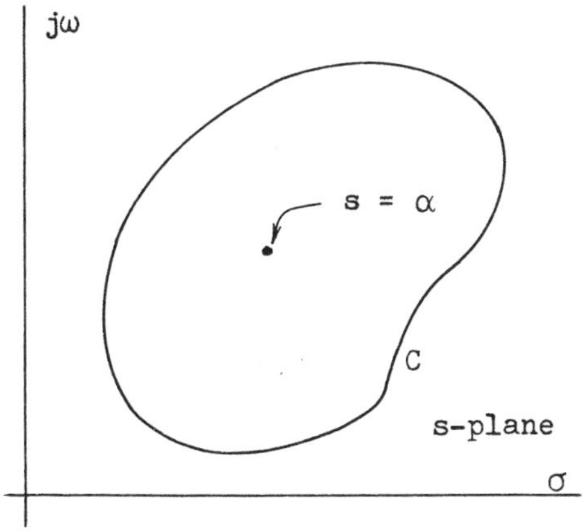

Figure 3-20. The Contour C.

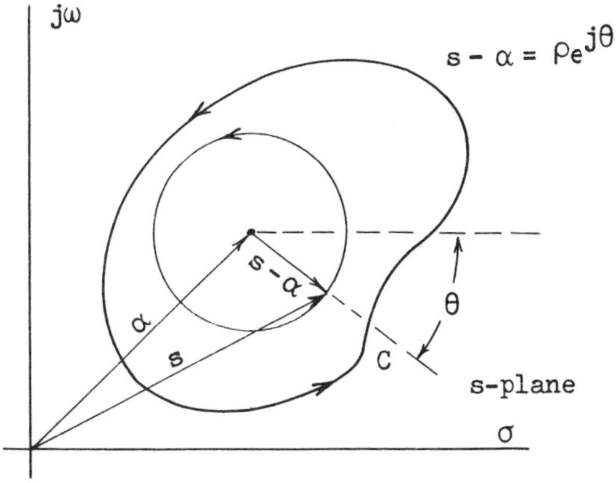

Figure 3-21. Adding the New Contour C'

In order to apply the principle of the Cauchy-Goursat theorem, a small circle C' is drawn with a radius ρ and centered at $s = \alpha$. (Figure 3-21). This produces a multiply-connected region. Therefore, since

$$s - \alpha = \rho e^{j\theta} \quad \text{and} \qquad 3\text{-}84$$

$$ds = j\rho e^{j\theta} \; d\theta, \text{ then} \qquad 3\text{-}85$$

$$\oint_C f(s) \cdot ds = \oint_C \frac{h(s)}{s-\alpha} \cdot ds = \oint_{C'} \frac{h(s)}{s-\alpha} \cdot ds = \oint_{C'} \frac{h(\alpha)}{e^{j\theta}} (j\rho e^{j\theta} d\theta) \,. \qquad 3\text{-}86$$

Now, the value of the integral is unchanged if ρ approaches zero, therefore,

$$\oint_{C'} f(s) \cdot ds = \oint_{C'} \frac{h(s)}{s-\alpha} ds = 2\pi j h(\alpha) \qquad 3\text{-}87$$

or

$$h(\alpha) = \frac{1}{2\pi j} \oint_C f(s) \cdot ds \qquad 3\text{-}88$$

where $f(s)$ has a simple isolated pole at $s = \alpha$. $h(\alpha)$ is called the "residue" of $f(s)$ at the simple pole α. Therefore, in association with a simple pole, α,

$$h(\alpha) = \begin{matrix}\text{the residue of} \\ f(s) \text{ at } \alpha\end{matrix} = \lim_{s \to \alpha} (s - \alpha) \cdot f(s) \,. \qquad 3\text{-}89$$

An important interpretation of the Cauchy-Integral formula is that for a function with a simple pole, the integral of the function around any contour enclosing only that pole (the function being analytic on the contour) is equal to $2\pi j$ times the residue of the function at that pole.

Example 3-7

Consider the function, $f(s) = \frac{20(s + 2)}{s(s + 10)}$. 3-90

This function is analytic everywhere except at the singular points (poles) $s = 0$, and $s = -10$. Now, suppose it is desired to evaluate the integral,

$\oint_{C_{-10}} f(s) \cdot ds$, around a contour enclosing only the pole at $s = -10$.

$$\oint_{C_{-10}} f(s) \cdot ds = 2\pi j(\text{Residue})_{-10} = 2\pi j \cdot \lim_{s \to -10}(s + 10) \cdot f(s) = 32\pi j. \quad 3\text{-}91$$

In addition, the residue of $f(s)$ at the pole, $s = 0$, would be

$$(\text{Residue})_0 = \lim_{s \to 0} s \cdot f(s) = 4. \quad 3\text{-}92$$

The value of the integral whose contour encloses both poles would be

$$\oint_C f(s) \cdot ds = 32\pi j + 2\pi j(4) = 40\pi j. \quad 3\text{-}93$$

3-17 The Residue Theorem

If $f(s)$ is analytic within and on C except for a finite number of poles, s_1, s_2, ..., s_n, inside C, then

$$\oint_C f(s) \cdot ds = 2\pi j \cdot (R_1 + R + ..., + R_i + ... + R_n) \quad 3\text{-}94$$

where R_i is the residue at the ith pole.

3-18 Residues

The discussion of paragraph (3-16) presented the fact that when a closed-contour integral is evaluated around a contour which encloses a pole, then the result is not zero, but rather yields a value called a "residue" times $2\pi j$. In other words,

$$\text{Residue} = \frac{1}{2\pi j} \oint f(s) \cdot ds. \qquad 3\text{-}95$$

If the pole, $s = \alpha$, is first order, the residue is

$$\text{Residue} = \lim_{s \to \alpha} (s - \alpha) \cdot f(s). \qquad 3\text{-}96$$

Now, consider the case when $f(s)$ has an mth order pole at $s = \alpha$.

$$f(s) = \frac{h(s)}{(s - \alpha)^m} \qquad 3\text{-}97$$

where $h(s)$ is analytic at $s = \alpha$. For purposes of ready reference, let it be stated at this point that the residue associated with a pole, α, of order m is

$$\text{Residue} = \frac{1}{(m-1)!} \left[\frac{d^{m-1}}{ds^{m-1}} (s - \alpha)^m \cdot f(s) \right]_{s = \alpha}. \qquad 3\text{-}98$$

In order to show one method of producing (3-98), let the procedure be to expand $h(s)$ about α in its Taylor's series. This is permissible since $h(s)$ is analytic at α and in a neighborhood of α.

$$h(s) = (s-\alpha)^m f(s) = \frac{h(\alpha)}{0!} + \frac{h'(\alpha) \cdot (s-\alpha)}{1!} + \ldots + \frac{h^{m-1}(\alpha) \cdot (s-\alpha)^{m-1}}{m-1)!} + \ldots \qquad 3\text{-}99$$

Dividing through by $(s - \alpha)^m$ yields

$$f(s) = \frac{h(\alpha)}{(s-\alpha)^m} + \frac{h'(\alpha)}{(s-\alpha)^{m-1}} + \frac{h''(\alpha)}{2!(s-\alpha)^{m-2}} + \dots + \frac{h^{m-1}(\alpha)}{(m-1)!(s-\alpha)} + \dots \qquad 3\text{-}100$$

which can be expressed in general as

$$f(s) = \underbrace{\frac{A_{-m}}{(s-\alpha)^m} + \frac{A_{-(m-1)}}{(s-\alpha)^{m-1}} + \dots + \frac{A_{-1}}{(s-\alpha)}}_{\text{Principle part}} + \underbrace{A_0 + A_1(s-\alpha) + \dots}_{\text{Regular part}} \qquad 3\text{-}101$$

(3-100) and (3-101) express the Laurent series for f(s) about α.

Now, $\frac{1}{2\pi j}\oint_C f(s) \cdot ds$ is the residue for the mth order pole, $s = \alpha$, 3-102

where C encloses the point α. Since f(s) is analytic on C, the integral of (3-102) is to be applied to both sides of (3-101), the right side of (3-101) being integrated term-by-term. The result of integrating the terms in the "regular" part will be zero since these terms are analytic within the contour C. It can also be shown that all terms in the "principle" part, with the exception of the A_{-1} term, will also be zero.[1] Consequently,

$$\oint_C f(s) \cdot ds = \oint_C \frac{A_{-1}}{(s-\alpha)} \cdot ds \qquad 3\text{-}103$$

and by application of Cauchy's Integral formula,

$$\oint_C \frac{A_{-1}}{(s-\alpha)} \cdot ds = 2\pi j \cdot A_{-1} \qquad 3\text{-}104$$

---

[1]Goldman, Transformation Calculus, 1949, p. 166.

Therefore, A_{-1} = the Residue. 3-105

Now, referring back to (3-100) and (3-101) it is seen that A_{-1} is equal to the coefficient of $1/(s-\alpha)$, namely,

$$A_{-1} = \frac{h^{m-1}(\alpha)}{(m-1)!}. \qquad 3\text{-}106$$

Applying (3-97), A_{-1}, the residue, becomes

$$\text{Residue} = \frac{1}{(m-1)!}\left[\frac{d^{m-1}}{ds^{m-1}}(s-\alpha)^m \cdot f(s)\right]_{s=\alpha}. \qquad 3\text{-}107$$

<u>Example 3-8</u>

For the function

$$f(s) = \frac{10(s+1)}{s^2(s+2)} \qquad 3\text{-}108$$

determine the residue at s = 0, (m = 2)

$$R_o = \frac{1}{(2-1)!}\left[\frac{d}{ds}\, s^2 \cdot f(s)\right]_{s=o} = \frac{d}{ds}\left[\frac{10(s+1)}{(s+2)}\right]_{s=o} = 2.5. \qquad 3\text{-}109$$

For the special case of m = 1, the general residue formula of (3-107) becomes

$$\text{Residue (first-order pole)} = (s-\alpha)\cdot f(s)\Big]_{s=\alpha} \qquad 3\text{-}110$$

which, of course, is identical to (3-89) developed in paragraph 3-16.

An alternate form for the calculation of the residue at a first-order pole will now be developed. This form is particularly useful when the denominator of f(s) is in unfactored form. Consider that

$$f(s) = \frac{P(s)}{Q(s)} \qquad 3\text{-}111$$

where P(s) and Q(s) are each, respectively, analytic and continuous at $s = \alpha$, and $P(\alpha) \neq 0$. Expanding P(s) and Q(s) in their Taylor's series at point α,

$$f(\alpha) = \frac{P(\alpha) + P'(\alpha)(s-\alpha) + \frac{P''(\alpha)(s-\alpha)^2}{2!} + \cdots}{Q(\alpha) + Q'(\alpha)(s-\alpha) + \frac{Q''(\alpha)(s-\alpha)^2}{2!} + \cdots} . \qquad 3\text{-}112$$

Since $s = \alpha$ is a first-order pole, then $Q(\alpha) = 0$. Multiplying through by $(s - \alpha)$ yields

$$(s-\alpha)\cdot f(\alpha) = \frac{P(\alpha) + P'(\alpha)(s-\alpha) + \frac{P''(\alpha)(s-\alpha)^2}{2!} + \cdots}{Q'(\alpha) + \frac{Q''(\alpha)(s-\alpha)^2}{2!} + \cdots} . \qquad 3\text{-}113$$

The higher order terms of (3-113) vanish as $s \to \alpha$, so it can be written,

$$\lim_{s\to\alpha} (s-\alpha)\cdot f(s) = \lim_{s\to\alpha} \frac{P(s)}{Q'(s)} = \text{Residue at } \alpha. \qquad 3\text{-}114$$

Example 3-9

It is known that $s = -2$ is a simple (first-order) pole of the function

$$f(s) = \frac{8(s+6)}{s^3 + 6s^2 + 8s} . \qquad 3\text{-}115$$

Find the residue at the pole, $s = -2$.

$$R_{-2} = \left.\frac{P(s)}{Q'(s)}\right|_{s=-2} = \left.\frac{8(s+6)}{3s^2 + 12s + 8}\right|_{s=-2} = \frac{32}{-4} = -8. \qquad 3\text{-}116$$

3-19 Evaluating Closed-Path Integrals Through the Use of Residues

In paragraph 3-16, it was shown that the value of an integral, whose contour enclosed a pole, was the residue at that pole. This rightly suggests, then, that closed-contour integrals may be evaluated by the application of the Cauchy-Goursat Theorem (3-82), and the subsequent summation of the residues of all the poles, respectively, enclosed by the contour. A classic example of the application of residues in this respect is the evaluation of the inverse Laplace transform integral. From the theory of the Laplace transform, the inverse transform of F(s) is

$$f(t) = \frac{1}{2\pi j} \cdot \oint_{\sigma_o - j\infty}^{\sigma_o + j\infty} F(s) \cdot e^{st} \cdot ds \, . \qquad 3\text{-}117$$

The contour of integration is understood to enclose all of the poles of F(s) (all of the interior poles of $F(s) \cdot e^{st}$) as indicated in Figure 3-22.

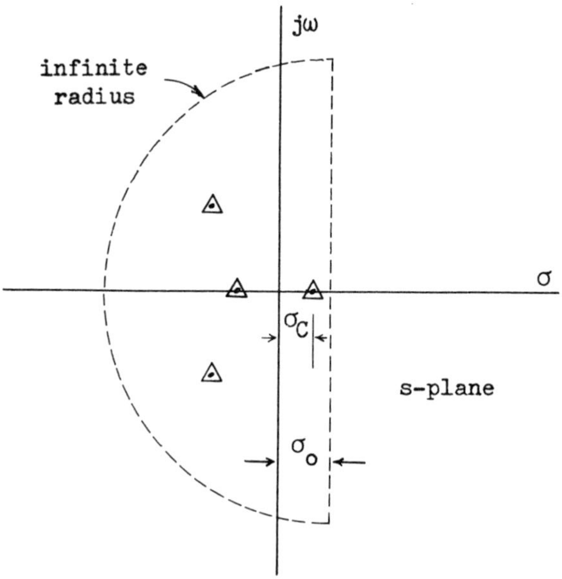

Figure 3-22. A Typical Contour for the Integral of (3-117)

It is apparent, then, that f(t) is in reality the summation of the residues of the s-function, namely, $F(s) \cdot e^{st}$. Referring to Figure 3-22, it is seen that σ_o must be large enough for the contour to enclose the rightmost interior pole of $F(s) \cdot e^{st}$. If the rightmost pole has a real part of σ_c, then $\sigma = \sigma_c$ is called the "abscissa of convergence," and σ_o must be greater than σ_c. So, the inversion integral of (3-117) may be evaluated through the application of the Cauchy-Goursat Theorem and the summation of the associated residues.

Example 3-10

Determine the inverse transform of

$$G(s) = \frac{4(s+2)}{s(s+4)} . \qquad \text{3-118}$$

Using (3-11),

$$f(t) = s\left[G(s) \cdot e^{st}\right]_{s=0} + (s+4)\left[G(s) \cdot e^{st}\right]_{s=-4} \qquad \text{3-119}$$

$$= \left.\frac{4(s+2)e^{st}}{s+4}\right]_{s=0} + \left.\frac{4(s+2)e^{st}}{s}\right]_{s=-4} \qquad \text{3-120}$$

$$= 2 + 2 \cdot e^{-4t} = 2(1 + e^{-4t}). \qquad \text{3-121}$$

Example 3-11

Determine the inverse transform of

$$G(s) = \frac{s}{(s+\alpha)^2} . \qquad \text{3-122}$$

This function has single pole of order 2 at $s = -\alpha$. (3-107) will have to be used.

$$f(t) = \frac{1}{(2-1)!}\left[\frac{d}{ds}(s+\alpha)^2 \cdot G(s) \cdot e^{st}\right]_{s=-\alpha} \qquad 3\text{-}123$$

$$= \frac{d}{ds}\, s \cdot e^{st}\Big]_{s=-\alpha} \qquad 3\text{-}124$$

$$= ste^{st} + e^{st}\Big]_{s=-\alpha} \qquad 3\text{-}125$$

$$= -\alpha te^{-\alpha t} + e^{-\alpha t} = (1-\alpha t)e^{-\alpha t}. \qquad 3\text{-}126$$

3-20 Partial Fractions

When preparing to determine the inverse Laplace transform of a rational function, it is frequently desirable to expand the function in partial fractions. This results in the form,

$$f(s) = f_1(s) + f_2(s) + \dots + f_n(s). \qquad 3\text{-}127$$

For example,

$$f(s) = \frac{8(s+2)}{(s+1)(s+5)^2\,(s+8)^3} \qquad 3\text{-}128$$

$$= \frac{A_{-3}}{(s+8)^3} + \frac{A_{-2}}{(s+8)^2} + \frac{A_{-1}}{(s+8)} + \frac{B_{-2}}{(s+5)^2} + \frac{B_{-1}}{(s+5)} + \frac{C_{-1}}{(s+1)}. \qquad 3\text{-}129$$

The right side of (3-127) and (3-129) is actually the sum of the principal parts of the Laurent expansions for f(s) at all of its poles, respectively. The principal part of the Laurent expansion at a pole of order m possesses m terms. The general form is shown in (3-101), and the coefficient A_{-1} is given by (3-107). Now, when expanding a function in partial fractions when one of its poles is order m, not only must the

A_{-1} coefficient be determined (or B_{-1}, or C_{-1}, as the case may be), but also A_{-2}, A_{-3}, ..., A_{-m}. An inspection of (3-101) and (3-100) will reveal that the various coefficients in the principal part of the Laurent expansion can be determined from

$$A_{-r} = \frac{1}{(m - r)!}\left[\frac{d^{m-r}}{ds^{m-r}}(s - \alpha)^m \cdot f(s)\right]_{s=\alpha} \qquad 3\text{-}130$$

where r is the absolute value of the subscript on the desired coefficient in the principal part of the Laurent expansion at the pole, $s = \alpha$, which has an order of m.

In order that the foregoing remarks apply, the rational s-function must approach zero as s approaches infinity. This means that the polynomial in the denominator must be of higher degree than the polynomial in the numerator. If a case is encountered where the numerator is of higher degree, then long division can be carried to the point where the remainder function meets the criteria, and then the partial fraction expansion is carried out on the remainder function.

Example 3-12

Expand the following function in partial fractions.

$$f(s) = \frac{10}{(s + 4)(s + 2)^3} \qquad 3\text{-}131$$

$$= \frac{A_{-3}}{(s + 2)^3} + \frac{A_{-2}}{(s + 2)^2} + \frac{A_{-1}}{(s + 2)} + \frac{B_{-1}}{(s + 4)} \cdot \qquad 3\text{-}132$$

Making use of (3-130), with $m = 3$,

$$A_{-3} = \frac{1}{0!}\left[(s + 2)^3 \cdot f(s)\right]_{s=-2} = \left[\frac{10}{s + 4}\right]_{s=-2} = 5 \qquad 3\text{-}133$$

$$A_{-2} = \frac{1}{1!}\left[\frac{d}{ds}(s+2)^3 \cdot f(s)\right]_{s=-2} = \left[\frac{-10}{(s+4)^2}\right]_{s=-2} = -2.5 \qquad 3\text{-}134$$

$$A_{-1} = \frac{1}{2!}\left[\frac{d^2}{ds^2}(s+2)^3 \cdot f(s)\right]_{s=-2} = \left[\frac{20}{2(s+4)^3}\right]_{s=-2} = 2.5 \qquad 3\text{-}135$$

$$B_{-1} = \left[(s+4) \cdot f(s)\right]_{s=-4} = \left[\frac{10}{(s+2)^3}\right]_{s=-4} = -\frac{5}{4}\,. \qquad 3\text{-}136$$

3-21 The Laplace Transform

For the sake of continuity, the following brief discussion will begin with the Fourier series. If f(t) is defined for all real time, and is periodic with a period T such that f(t + T) = f(t) for all time, then f(t) may be represented by an infinite series of harmonically related terms, namely,

$$f(t) = \frac{A_o}{2} + \sum_{n=1}^{n=\infty}(A_n \cdot \cos n\omega t + B_n \cdot \sin n\omega t) \qquad 3\text{-}137$$

where

$$A_n = \frac{2}{T}\int_o^T f(t) \cdot \cos n\omega t \qquad 3\text{-}138$$

$$B_n = \frac{2}{T}\int_o^T f(t) \cdot \sin(n\omega t)dt \qquad 3\text{-}139$$

where

$$\omega = 2\pi/T. \qquad 3\text{-}140$$

Now, by allowing the period T to become infinite, the result leads to the Fourier transform which is useful for nonperiodic functions.

$$F(j\omega) = \int_{t=-\infty}^{t=\infty} f(t) \cdot e^{-j\omega t}dt \qquad 3\text{-}141$$

$$f(t) = \frac{1}{2\pi} \int_{\omega=-\infty}^{\omega=\infty} F(j\omega) \cdot e^{j\omega t} d\omega. \qquad 3\text{-}142$$

The transform of (3-141) transforms the nonperiodic function f(t) into a function of frequency, F(jω), thereby yielding the "frequency spectrum" corresponding to f(t). (3-142) is called the inverse Fourier transform in that a function of frequency is transformed into its corresponding function of time.

The Fourier transform may be used in connection with studies of systems in much the same way the Laplace transform is used; however, many of the functions associated with these studies lead to problems of convergence of the Fourier integral. In order to sidestep this problem, f(t) will now be assumed to always have the factor $e^{-\sigma t}$ associated with it. If σ is large enough (see Figure 3-22), then $f(t) \cdot e^{-\sigma t}$ will produce convergence. In addition, application of the transform will be limited to positive time. Therefore, (3-141) becomes

$$\int_0^\infty f(t) \cdot e^{-\sigma t} e^{-j\omega t} dt = \int_0^\infty f(t) \cdot e^{-(\sigma + j\omega)t} dt = F(\sigma + j\omega). \qquad 3\text{-}143$$

And, if σ + jω is replaced by s

$$F(s) = \int_0^\infty f(t) \cdot e^{-st} dt, \text{ the Laplace transform.} \qquad 3\text{-}144$$

Correspondingly, (3-142) becomes

$$f(t) = \frac{1}{2\pi j} \int_{\sigma_0 - j\infty}^{\sigma_0 + j\infty} F(s) \cdot s^{st} ds, \text{ the inverse Laplace transform.} \qquad 3\text{-}145$$

Comparing the Fourier transform and the Laplace transform, it is seen that when applicable, the Fourier transform transforms a given time function into a function of real frequency; whereas, the Laplace transform transforms the time function into a function of "complex frequency."

APPENDIX I

BIBLIOGRAPHY

1. Churchhill, R. V. Introduction to Complex Variables and Applications. 2nd ed, New York: McGraw-Hill Book Company, Inc., 1960.

2. Churchhill, R. V. Operational Mathematics. 2nd ed, New York: McGraw-Hill Book Company, Inc., 1958.

3. Craig, Edward J. Laplace and Fourier Transforms for Electrical Engineers. New York: Holt, Rinehart, and Winston, Inc., 1964.

4. Gardner and Barnes. Transients in Linear Systems. Vol. 1. New York: John Wiley and Sons, Inc., 1953.

5. Goldman, S. Transformation Calculus and Electrical Transients. New York: Prentice-Hall, Inc., 1949.

6. Lepage, W. R. Complex Variables and the Laplace Transform for Engineers. New York: McGraw-Hill Book Company, Inc., 1961.

7. Lepage and Seely. General Network Analysis. New York: McGraw-Hill Book Company, Inc., 1952.

8. Nixon, F. E. Handbook of Laplace Transforms. Englewood Cliffs, New Jersey: Prentice-Hall, Inc., 1960.

9. Savant, C. J. Fundamentals of Laplace Transformation. New York: McGraw-Hill Book Company, Inc., 1962.

10. Sokolnikoff and Redheffer. Mathematics of Physics and Modern Engineering. New York: McGraw-Hill Book Company, Inc., 1958.

$$\frac{C_1}{(S+2)^3} + \frac{C_2}{(S+2)^2} + \frac{C_3}{(S+2)}$$

$$C_3 = \frac{1}{(m-1)!} \frac{d^{m-1}}{ds^{m-1}} \left[\frac{N(S)}{D(S)} (S+2)^3 \right]_{S=-r_1}$$

3

m stays 3